KU-566-640

Thermodynamic Assessment of Rocket Engines

B. A. NIKOLAYEV

Translated by

W. E. JONES

United Kingdom
Atomic Energy Authority

Translation edited by

B. P. MULLINS

Senior Principal Scientific Officer
Ministry of Aviation
Farnborough, Hants

THE ROYAL COLLEGE OF SCIENCE AND TECHNOLOGY
ANDERSONIAN LIBRARY
GLASGOW

D
621.4356
NIK

PERGAMON PRESS

OXFORD · LONDON · NEW YORK · PARIS

1963

52355
27.5.64

PERGAMON PRESS LTD.
Headington Hill Hall, Oxford
4 and 5 Fitzroy Square, London, W.1

PERGAMON PRESS INC.
122 East 55th Street, New York 22, N.Y.

GAUTHIER-VILLARS ED.
55 Quai des Grands-Augustins, Paris, 6e

PERGAMON PRESS G.m.b.H.
Kaiserstrasse 75, Frankfurt am Main

Distributed in the Western Hemisphere by
THE MACMILLAN COMPANY . NEW YORK
pursuant to a special arrangement with
Pergamon Press Limited

Copyright © 1963
PERGAMON PRESS LTD.

Library of Congress Catalog Card Number 63-10132

This is a translation of the original Russian
Termodinamicheskii raschet raketnykh dvigatelei
published in 1960 by Oborongiz, Moscow

621.438

MADE IN GREAT BRITAIN

INTERNATIONAL SERIES OF MONOGRAPHS IN

AERONAUTICS AND ASTRONAUTICS

DIVISION VII: AERODYNAMICS

Editor : Professor A. D. BAXTER

VOLUME 4

THERMODYNAMIC ASSESSMENT OF ROCKET ENGINES

OTHER TITLES IN THE DIVISION ON AERODYNAMICS

Vol. 1. Scorer — *NATURAL AERODYNAMICS*
Vol. 2. Landahl — *UNSTEADY TRANSONIC FLOW*
Vol. 3. Guderley — *THE THEORY OF TRANSONIC FLOW*

OTHER DIVISION IN THE SERIES ON AERONAUTICS AND ASTRONAUTICS

SOLID AND STRUCTURAL MECHANICS

PROPULSION SYSTEMS INCLUDING FUELS

AVIONICS

AVIATION AND SPACE MEDICINE

FLIGHT TESTING

ASTRONAUTICS

MATERIALS, SCIENCE AND ENGINEERING

SYMPOSIA

INTERNATIONAL SERIES OF MONOGRAPHS IN AERONAUTICS AND ASTRONAUTICS

CHAIRMEN

Th. von KARMAN
Advisory Group for Aeronautical Research and Development
North Atlantic Treaty Organization, 64 rue de Varenne, Paris VIIe France

H. L. DRYDEN
Deputy Administrator National Aeronautics and Space Administration
Washington 25, D. C.
U. S. A.

HONORARY ADVISORY BOARD

UNITED KINGDOM

A. M. Ballantyne
A. D. Baxter
W. Cawood
J. S. Clarke
Sir H. Roxbee Cox
Sir W. S. Farren
G. W. H. Gardner
W. S. Hemp
S. G. Hooker
E. T. Jones
W. P. Jones
G. B. Lachmann
A. A. Lombard
B. P. Mullins
A. J. Murphy
L. F. Nicholson
F. W. Page
Sir A. G. Pugsley
H. B. Squire
L. H. Sterne
A. D. Young

UNITED STATES

H. J. Allen
M. Alperin
R. L. Bisplinghoff
W. von Braun
F. H. Clauser
M. U. Clauser
J. R. Dempsey
W. S. Diehl
C. S. Draper
A. Ferri
C. C. Furnas
C. Gazley, Jr.
E. Haynes
E. H. Heinemann
N. J. Hoff
C. Kaplan
J. Kaplan
J. Keto
W. B. Klemperer
E. Kotcher
E. H. Krause
Col. N. L. Krisberg
A. K. Kuethe
J. P. Layton
L. Lees
B. Lewis
P. A. Libby
H. W. Liepmann
J. R. Markham
C. B. Millikan
W. F. Milliken, Jr
W. C. Nelson
W. H. Pickering
R. W. Porter
L. E. Root
G. S. Schairer
F. R. Shanley
E. R. Sharp
S. F. Singer
C. R. Soderberg
J. Stack
M. Stern
H. G. Stever
G. P. Sutton
R. J. Thompson
L. A. Wood
T. P. Wright
M. J. Zucrow

POLAND

F. Misztal

GERMANY

G. Bock
H. Görtler
O. Lutz
A. W. Quick

AUSTRALIA

L. P. Coombes

BELGIUM

J. Ducarme

ITALY

G. Gabrielli

CANADA

J. J. Green
H. C. Luttman
D. C. MacPhail
D. L. Mordell

SWEDEN

B. K. L. Lundberg

HOLLAND

H. J. van der Maas
C. Zwikker

FRANCE

L. Malavard
M. Roy

SPAIN

Col. Pérez-Marín

JAPAN

I. Tani

RUSSIA

A. A. Ilyushin

ТЕРМОДИНАМИЧЕСКИЙ РАСЧЕТ РАКЕТНЫХ ДВИГАТЕЛЕЙ

Б. А. НИКОЛАЕВ

Contents

Legend adopted

α_0	— Excess oxidant coefficient;
α	— Excess oxygen coefficient;
C_c, H_c, N_c, O_c	— Content by weight of chemical elements per kg of combustible, expressed in g;
C_o, H_o, N_o, O_o	— Content by weight of chemical elements per kg of oxidant, expressed in g;
q_c, q_o	— Proportion by weight of combustible and oxidant per kg fuel;
ν_0	— Theoretical ratio of components (number of weight units of oxidant necessary for the complete oxidation of one weight unit of combustible);
ν	— Actual ratio of components (number of weight units of oxidant required by one weight unit of combustible for a given α_0);
A_C, A_H, A_N, A_O	— Number of g-atoms of carbon, hydrogen, nitrogen and oxygen respectively in 1 kg of fuel;
M^0, M	— Number of moles in 1 kg respectively of undissociated and of dissociated combustion products;
μ_k^0, μ_k	— Average ("apparent") molecular weight respectively of the undissociated and of the dissociated combustion products;
$X_C = X_C^0$; $X_H = X_H^0$ $X_N = X_N^0$; $X_O = X_O^0$	— Parameters characterizing the composition of a fuel;
Q_{comb}	— Heat of combustion of a substance (determined from handbooks);
Q_{form}	— Heat of formation of a substance (determined from handbooks);
p^0, p	— Pressure of undissociated and dissociated combustion products respectively, in atm;
T_0	— Temperature of combustion of fuel in the absence of dissociation of the combustion products, in °K;
i_f, i_c, i_o	— Enthalpy of 1 kg respectively of fuel, combustible and oxidant, in kcal/kg;
$T_{c \cdot c}$, T_{exh}	— Temperature of the combustion products in the combustion chamber of the engine and in the exhaust section of the nozzle respectively, in °K;
$S_{c \cdot c}$, S_{exh}	— Entropy of combustion products in the combustion chamber of the engine and in the exhaust section of the nozzle respectively, in kcal/kg. deg;
i_H^0, i_H	— Enthalpy of undissociated and dissociated com-

bustion products respectively in temperature region H (2800–3800°K), in kcal/kg;

i^0_L, i_L — Enthalpy of undissociated and dissociated combustion products respectively in temperature region (1400–2800°K), in kcal/kg;

$c^0_{p,H}$, $c^0_{p,L}$ — Specific heat of undissociated combustion products in temperature regions H and L respectively, in kcal/kg·deg;

$p^p_{H_2O_{2800}}$ — Partial pressure of water vapour in the undissociated combustion products at a temperature of 2800°K, in atm;

i^0_{2800} — Enthalpy of 1 kg of undissociated combustion products at a temperature of 2800°K, in kcal/kg;

$i_{T_{c\cdot c}}$, i_{exh} — Enthalpy of 1 kg of combustion products in the combustion chamber of the engine (at a temperature $T_{c\cdot c}$) and in the exhaust section of the nozzle respectively, in kcal/kg;

i^0_v — Parameter characterizing the enthalpy of the undissociated combustion products at a temperature of 2800°K;

v^0, v — Specific volume of the undissociated and dissociated combustion products respectively, in m^3/kg;

Δi — Increase in enthalpy of 1 kg of combustion products as a result of their dissociation, in kcal/kg;

$\Delta i^{(40)}_H$ — Increase in enthalpy of 1 kg of combustion products as a result of their dissociation in temperature region H at a pressure of 40 atm, in kcal/kg;

$\Delta i^{(1)}_L$ — Increase in enthalpy of 1 kg of combustion products as a result of their dissociation in temperature region L at a pressure of 1 atm, in kcal/kg;

$\Delta i^{(40)}_{H,v}$ — Parameter characterizing the increase in enthalpy as a result of dissociation of the combustion products in temperature region H at a pressure $p = 40$ atm;

$\Delta i^{(1)}_{L,v}$ — Parameter characterizing the increase in enthalpy as a result of dissociation of the combustion products in temperature region L at a pressure $p = 1$ atm;

$\Delta i^{(3400)}_{H,v}$ — Parameter characterizing the increase in enthalpy as a result of dissociation of the combustion products in temperature region H at a temperature of 3400°K;

$\Delta i^{(2800)}_{L,v}$ — Parameter, characterizing the increase in enthalpy as a result of dissociation of the combustion products in temperature region L at a temperature of 2800°K;

Δi_H — Increase in enthalpy as a result of dissociation of 1 kg of combustion products in temperature region H, at a temperature T and pressure p in kcal/kg;

Δi_L — Increase in enthalpy as a result of dissociation of 1 kg of combustion products in temperature region L, at a temperature T and pressure p in kcal/kg;

$\Delta i_{H, v \Phi}$ — Parameter characterizing the increase in enthalpy of the combustion products as a result of dissociation at the fixed temperature $T_{H \Phi} = 3400$°K and pressure $p_{H, \Phi} = 40$ atm;

$\Delta i_{L, v, \Phi}$ — Parameter characterizing the increase in enthalpy of the combustion products as a result of dissociation at the fixed temperature $T_{L, \Phi} = 2800$°K and pressure $p_{L, \Phi} = 1$ atm;

m_H, m_L — Power index in formulae describing the dependence of parameters connected with dissociation on the temperature of the combustion products (in regions H and L respectively);

n_{eff} — Effective power index in formulae describing the dependence of parameters connected with dissociation on the pressure of the combustion products.

q — Ratio of increase in enthalpy of the combustion products as a result of dissociation to the increase in the number of moles;

ω — Relative increase in pressure of the combustion products as a result of dissociation taking place at constant volume of the combustion products;

S_H, S_L — Entropy of combustion products in temperature regions H L respectively;

W_{exh} — Ideal exhaust velocity of the combustion products from the nozzle of an engine, in m/sec;

P_{sp} — Specific thrust of an engine, in kg · sec/kg;

k — Adiabatic flow index;

B_1, B_2 — Parameters characterizing the intensity of progress of dissociation reactions;

n_0, n — Ratio of partial pressure of water vapour to the partial pressure of diatomic hydrogen in the undissociated and dissociated combustion products respectively.

Translation Editor's Preface

THE scope of this book can be gauged from the Foreword and the Contents list. The treatment of the subject begins as usual with a statement of the equations of mass conservation and of chemical equilibrium for rocket combustion gases, firstly with no dissociation, and secondly with dissociation. Detailed methods of calculating the various thermodynamic quantities of interest including the selection and indeed the construction of primary parameters for this purpose differ from author to author. The method adopted by the present author and expounded, together with a number of fully worked examples, in this monograph is effective, rapid and reasonably accurate. Following five tables of numerical data, some forty families of curves are presented which, though not large in area, are printed clearly; these render the monograph to a considerable extent self-contained. This book should be of interest and use to rocket performance engineers and is sufficiently elementary to be read by students of jet propulsion science.

B. P. MULLINS

Foreword

In constructing a flying machine (aeroplane, rocket) it is essential to build a version of the power unit which is the best for a given set of circumstances. One of the most important problems for this is the choice of the fuel on which the engine should operate, and the designation of its operating régime.

The choice of fuel (combustible, oxidant and their ratios) and of the operating régime of the engine (pressure of the combustion products in the combustion chamber and in the discharge section of the nozzle) is undertaken on the basis of numerous thermodynamical calculations for the engine. The primary aim of these calculations is to determine the value of the specific thrust — the most important operating characteristic of rocket engines. The well-known methods of thermodynamical calculation of rocket engines, based on the preliminary calculation of the chemical composition of the combustion products, are complex and laborious. Consequently, it is expedient to use approximation methods of calculation which enable sufficiently accurate results to be obtained.

In the present book an approximation method for the thermodynamical calculation of rocket engines is proposed which does not require the preliminary calculation of the composition of the combustion products, and its application is considered in cases most frequently encountered in practice. The proposed method holds good for the calculation of the operating characteristics of rocket engines with fuels consisting of carbon, hydrogen, nitrogen and oxygen. Its accuracy is verified by more accurate methods of calculation for cases when the pressure of the combustion products in the combustion chamber is varied within the range from 20 to 100 atm, the pressure in the discharge section of the nozzle is reduced to 0·4–0·5 atm, the temperature of the combustion products attains 3800–4000°K. For this, the chemical elements are contained in the following quantities:

Carbon	from 4	to 40	per cent
Hydrogen	from 0·5	to 13	per cent
Nitrogen	from 0	to 80	per cent
Oxygen	from 15	to 85	per cent

The excess oxygen factor a is found to be within the range from 0·55 to 0·95*. It is connected with the more usual parameter — the excess oxidant factor a_0 by the following relationship:

$$a_0 = \frac{1}{v_0} \frac{\frac{8}{3} C_c + 8H_c - \frac{O_c}{a}}{\frac{O_0}{a} - \frac{8}{3} C_0 - 8H_0} .$$

For calculations carried out within the range of variation of chemical composition of the fuel, pressure and temperature of the combustion products recommended above, the magnitude of the error for the specific thrust in the overwhelming majority of cases does not exceed 0·5–1·0.

The magnitude of the error in the temperature of the combustion products does not exceed 30–50°. This assertion results from a number of check comparative calculations carried out for cases of the combustion products from fuels with widely differing ultimate analyses.

The approximation method of calculation of rocket engines is used to the best advantage in those cases when the well-known methods of calculation require the carrying out of an extremely large computing task. First and foremost are discussed calculations carried out with the purpose of comparatively analysing the operating characteristics of an engine using various fuels and at different régimes. These calculations are essential for choosing the most efficient fuel for the development of an engine, for designating the operating régime of the engine and also for devising new types of fuels. With a relatively small volume of calculation, and by carrying out the calculation on logarithmic 50 cm ruled paper, the answer to all the problems raised above can be obtained with a sufficient degree of accuracy.

If extremely accurate values for the thermodynamic parameters of the combustion products of the specified rocket fuels are essential, and likewise values for the specific thrusts, then the proposed method may also be useful. In this case it is recommended that the approximate values of these parameters be determined and then the accurate solution can be found by using the usual methods of successive approximations.

* The excess oxygen factor, as is well-known, defines the ratio of the actual content of oxygen in the fuel to the quantity required for the complete combustion of the combustible elements contained in the fuel: $a = \frac{A_O}{2A_C + 0{\cdot}5A_H}$

In the present book, a new method of calculating the chemical composition of the combustion products of rocket fuels is also given. It holds good for the combustion products of the same fuels for which we use the approximation method for the thermodynamical assessment of rocket engines developed by us. The proposed method of calculating the chemical composition of the combustion products of rocket engines is simpler in numerical behaviour than are the methods generally used. In order to facilitate the numerical workings by this method, subsidiary families of curves are introduced.

Introduction

THE specific thrust is determined first and foremost by the fuel being used, but it also depends substantially on the design and operating régime of the rocket engine. It is well known that the processes of combustion of the fuel and the discharge of the gases — the combustion products from the combustion chambers of rocket engines — are complex and inadequately studied. In connection with this, there is still no rigorous mathematical device which enables the specific thrust to be calculated, taking into account the losses arising as a result of operation of the actual engines.

Thermodynamical calculations are carried out, as a rule, without taking into account any energy losses, apart from losses dependent upon dissociation processes taking place in the combustion products (disintegration of the combustion products into more simple mono- or bi-atomic components under the action of high temperature). The calculated value of the specific thrust, determined without taking losses into account, will be greater than the actual value obtained by firing tests of the engines. However, in that case when the engine is designed correctly, the discrepancy between the calculated and actual values of the specific thrust does not exceed a few per cent. In the case of a given test the actual value of the specific thrust may be found from its calculated value by means of a simple conversion — by multiplying the calculated value of the specific thrust by a certain factor less than 1. The value of this factor is determined practically.

Thermodynamical performance calculations of rocket engines are usually carried out with the following assumptions. The intermixing of the fuel components prior to combustion is taken to be ideal, and the combustion of the fuel is taken to be complete. The heat content of the combustion products in the combustion chamber of the engine is taken to be equal to the heat content of the fuel. By choosing the pressure of the combustion products in the combustion chamber of the engine the specified condition enables their temperature to be calculated.

The process of expansion of the combustion products and their discharge from the engine is assumed to take place without friction, or supply of energy from outside or loss to the surroundings. For this it is assumed that the components of the combustion products exist in a state of chemical and energy equilibrium. What has been said above is equivalent to asserting that the process of expansion of the combustion products and their discharge from a rocket engine is subject to an isentropic law. The entropy of the combustion products in the discharge section of the nozzle is assumed to be equal to their entropy in the combustion chamber. By choosing the pressure of the combustion products in the discharge section of the nozzle, the latter condition enables their temperature in this section to be calculated, and consequently also their heat content.

The kinetic energy of the jet of discharging gases — the combustion products — is evolved as a consequence of the reduction of heat content of these products. For an ideal development of the processes of combustion and discharge the theoretical discharge velocity is determined by the equation

$$w_{\text{dis}} = 91.53 \sqrt{(i_f - i_{\text{dis}})}\,,$$

where i_{dis} is the heat content of the combustion products in the discharge section of the nozzle for an isentropic discharge process;

i_{f} is the heat content of the fuel.

The theoretical specific thrust for a calculated operating régime of the nozzle, for which the pressure of the combustion products in the discharge section of the nozzle is equal to atmospheric pressure, will be

$$P_{\text{sp}} = \frac{w_{\text{dis}}}{g}\,.$$

In future we shall call the theoretical specific thrust simply the specific thrust.

As the basis for the proposed method of engine assessment are assumed the approximate mathematical relationships, established by us, between the heat content and the entropy of the combustion products, their pressure and temperature, and also the initial ultimate analysis of the fuel. These relationships are established in two stages: first of all the relationships were obtained for undissociated and then dissociated combustion products. By undissociated combustion products of the fuels being considered were understood combustion products consisting only of carbon monoxide, carbon dioxide gas, water vapour, diatomic hydrogen and diatomic nitrogen. The numerical coefficients in the approximate mathematical expressions are determined on the basis of data in Table 1 for the heat content of the combustion products, given in the Appendix.

The heat content zero value can be chosen quite arbitrarily, but for establishing the heat content of the individual components of the combustion products it is necessary to take into account the possibility of chemical reactions taking place between them. Consequently, for all substances participating in the process (components of the fuel and of the combustion products), only one datum point should be adopted. The special feature of the heat content datum used in the book consists in the fact that the heat content of carbon dioxide gas, water vapour, diatomic hydrogen and nitrogen at 0°K is taken to be equal to zero. Since the thermal energy of the remaining components of the combustion products at 0°K are also equal to zero, then the chemical energy of these components at 0°K is defined as the heat of their formation from CO_2, H_2O, O_2 and N_2, reduced to absolute zero of temperature.

In using the proposed method for the assessment of rocket engines, the heat content of the fuel should be based on the same system of heat contents, which is adopted for the heat content of the combustion products. If there are data on the heat content of fuel components calculated on the basis of a different datum, then they should be reduced to that accepted in the present book. The method of calculation of the heat content of the fuel components and of the fuel as a whole is given at the end of the book in Section 20.

CHAPTER 1

Thermodynamic parameters of undissociated products of combustion

1. Undissociated Combustion Products

The combustion products in rocket engines are dissociated in the majority of cases, by virtue of the high temperatures. The composition of the dissociated combustion products depends not only on the initial chemical composition of the fuel and on their temperature, but also on the pressure. If it be assumed that the pressure of the combustion products increases infinitely then their composition tends to a wholly finite limit. The combustion products of the fuels under consideration consist in this case of water vapour H_2O, diatomic hydrogen H_2, carbon dioxide gas CO_2, carbon monoxide CO, and diatomic nitrogen N_2 (if oxidation reactions of the nitrogen be disregarded).

The content of one or other gas in unit weight of the combustion products is determined only by the initial chemical composition of the fuel and by the temperature of the combustion products. Under the conditions of infinitely large pressure all reactions which would occur with an increase in the number of moles (with an increase in volume) are suppressed. In this case it is possible for chemical reactions to take place which can proceed without change in the number of moles, and on which the magnitude of the pressure exerts no influence. The most characteristic reaction of this type taking place in the combustion products of the fuels under consideration is the reaction for the formation of water-gas

$$CO + H_2O \leftrightarrows CO_2 + H_2 . \tag{1.1}$$

The relative concentrations of the components of the combustion products, resulting from the change in temperature, will be changed in accordance with this reaction. The equilibrium equation for the reaction (1.1), expressed via the partial pressures of the combustion products, has the form

$$K = \frac{p^0_{CO_2}\, p^0_{H_2}}{p^0_{CO}\, p^0_{H_2O}} = f(T). \tag{1.2}$$

The numerical value of the equilibrium constant depends only on the temperature, and for a given reaction it is reduced as a result of increase in the latter. As a result of this, the concentration of water vapour and carbon monoxide in the combustion products is increased in consequence of the reduction in concentration of the carbon dioxide and diatomic hydrogen. The concentration of diatomic nitrogen remains invariable with change of temperature. The superscript "0" indicates that the given parameter refers to the combustion products, the chemical composition of which corresponds to an infinitely large pressure.

If it be arbitrarily assumed, in order to calculate the composition of the combustion products for any final pressure, that they consist only of H_2O, H_2, CO_2, CO and N_2, then the quantity of the components of the combustion products and their relative concentrations at a given temperature will be independent of the magnitude of the pressure and will be almost the same as in the case of an infinitely large pressure.

The combustion products, the calculation of which is carried out for the conditions indicated, will be known in future as the undissociated combustion products. For uniformity of presentation of the material in this book, the concentrations of the components of the undissociated combustion products in equation (1.2) and in future will be expressed via their partial pressures. The relationship between the number of moles of a certain ith component of the combustion products M_i^0 and its partial pressure p_i^0 is found according to the well-known relationship

$$\frac{p_i^0}{p^0} = \frac{M_i^0}{M^0}. \tag{1.3}$$

Since

$$M^0 = \frac{1000}{\mu_k^0}, \tag{1.4}$$

where μ_k^0 is the "apparent" (average) molecular weight of the mixture of combustion products, then, denoting

$$\mu^0 = \frac{\mu_k^0}{1000}, \tag{1.5}$$

we obtain finally

$$p_i^0 = p^0 \mu^0 M_i^0 . \tag{1.6}$$

The value of the parameter μ^0 is computed according to the elementary chemical composition of the fuel in the following manner. For the combustion of 1 g-atom of carbon, a total of 1 mole of carbon dioxide gas and carbon monoxide is formed, for the combustion of 1 g-atom of hydrogen a total of 0·5 moles of water vapour and diatomic hydrogen is formed, and from 1 g-atom of nitrogen is formed 0·5 moles of diatomic nitrogen. Consequently, for the combustion of 1 kg of fuel in which are contained A_C, A_H and A_N g-atoms of carbon, hydrogen and nitrogen respectively, a mole of combustion products is formed thus:

$$M^0 = A_C + 0{\cdot}5\,(A_H + A_N). \tag{1.7}$$

By joint consideration of expressions (1.4), (1.5), and (1.7) we obtain

$$\mu^0 = \frac{1}{A_C + 0{\cdot}5\,(A_H + A_N)} . \tag{1.8}$$

The parameter μ^0 is entirely determined by the composition of the fuel and remains invariable for changes in pressure and temperature of the combustion products.

In order to calculate the temperature of the undissociated combustion products it is necessary to form a system of algebraic equations in which the number of equations should be equal to the number of unknowns. The total number of unknown quantities is six, namely, five partial pressures of the combustion products comprising the gaseous mixture, and the temperature of combustion. Consequently, the system should consist of not less than six equations.

The equation for the equilibrium constant of the water gas formation reaction is used as one of these equations. Further the four equations of material balance are taken into consideration (the number of equations of material balance is equal to the number of chemical elements entering into the composition of the fuel).

The principle of developing the equation of material balance can be followed by the example of the chemical element oxygen. In 1 kg of fuel there are contained A_O g-atoms of oxygen. The combustion products — carbon dioxide gas, carbon monoxide and water vapour — also contain oxygen. In 1 mole of CO_2 are contained 2 g-atoms of oxygen, in 1 mole of CO there is 1 g-atom, and in 1 mole of H_2O there is also

1 g-atom of oxygen. On the basis of the Law of Conservation of Matter, the number of g-atoms of oxygen is the same in 1 kg of fuel as in 1 kg of combustion products; consequently

$$A_O = 2M^0_{CO_2} + M^0_{CO} + M^0_{H_2O}. \tag{1.9}$$

Let us transform equation (1.9). We shall multiply the right- and left-hand sides by $p^0 \mu^0$ and denote the product of the parameters of the left-hand side by X^0_O:

$$X^0_O = p^0 \mu^0 A_O. \tag{1.10}$$

Taking into consideration (1.6) we finally obtain

$$X^0_O = 2p^0_{CO_2} + p^0_{CO} + p^0_{H_2O}. \tag{1.11}$$

For the three other chemical elements, the equations of material balance are obtained similarly:

$$X^0_C = p^0_{CO_2} + p^0_{CO}; \tag{1.12}$$

$$X^0_H = 2p^0_{H_2O} + 2p^0_{H_2}; \tag{1.13}$$

$$X^0_N = 2p^0_{N_2}. \tag{1.14}$$

Here, by analogy with the parameter X^0_O, the symbols X^0_C, X^0_H and X^0_N denote:

$$X^0_C = p^0 \mu^0 A_C; \tag{1.15}$$

$$X^0_H = p^0 \mu^0 A_H; \tag{1.16}$$

$$X^0_N = p^0 \mu^0 A_N. \tag{1.17}$$

The equation of equality of enthalpy (heat content) of unit weight of fuel with the enthalpy of the combustion products will be the sixth and last equation in the system being considered. Assuming that heat losses are absent in the combustion of the fuel, we can write

$$i_T = i^0_{T_0}. \tag{1.18}$$

Here $i^0_{T_0}$ is the enthalpy of 1 kg of undissociated combustion products at the temperature of combustion T_0.

In that case, if the composition of the combustion products is known, the enthalpy $i^0_{T_0}$ can be determined by the equation

$$i^0_{T_0} = \frac{1}{p^0 \mu^0} (I_{CO_2} p^0_{CO_2} + I_{CO} p^0_{CO} + I_{H_2} p^0_{H} + I_{H_2O} p^0_{H_2O} + I_{N_2} p^0_{N_2}), \tag{1.18a}$$

where I_{CO_2}, I_{CO} and similar symbols are here and henceforth the values of the enthalpics of the components at a given temperature in kcal/mole according to Table 1 in the Appendix.

We bring together the equations so obtained into the one system:

$$\left.\begin{aligned} K &= \frac{p^0_{CO_2} p^0_{H_2}}{p^0_{CO} p^0_{H_2O}} = f(T); \\ X^0_O &= 2p^0_{CO_2} + p^0_{CO} + p^0_{H_2O} \\ X^0_C &= p^0_{CO_2} + p^0_{CO}; \\ X^0_H &= 2p^0_{H_2O} + 2p^0_{H_2}; \\ X^0_N &= 2p^0_{N_2}; \\ i_T &= i^0_{T_0}. \end{aligned}\right\} \qquad (1.19)$$

The most rational method of solving this system of equations consists in the following. It is necessary to assign a number of values for temperatures close to the anticipated temperature of combustion T_0, and for each chosen value of temperature to find the partial pressure of the combustion products, and also the enthalpy of their mixture [according to equation (1.18a)].

Equation (1.18) serves for verifying the accuracy of choice of temperature, which will be satisfied only in the case if the chosen temperature should be equal to T_0. In order to speed up the calculation, a supplementary graph is usually plotted of the dependence of the enthalpy of the combustion products on temperature and the sought-for temperature T_0 is determined from it.

The solution of the system of equations (1.19) for a predetermined temperature enables this system to be reduced to a quadratic equation relative to the partial pressure of any one of the combustion products (except for diatomic nitrogen). The partial pressure of diatomic nitrogen is determined directly from equation (1.41). For better continuity with the material set forth in the subsequent chapters, we shall solve the quadratic equation relative to the parameter $n_0 = p^0_{H_2O}/p^0_{H_2}$:

$$a_1 n_0^2 + b_1 n_0 + c_1 = 0, \qquad (1.20)$$

where

$$a_1 = K(2X^0_C - X^0_O + 0{\cdot}5X^0_H);$$

$$b_1 = K(2X^0_C - X^0_O) + X^0_C - X^0_O + 0{\cdot}5X^0_H;$$

$$c_1 = X^0_C - X^0_O.$$

The partial pressures of the components of the combustion products will be equal to:

$$p^0_{H_2} = \frac{0{\cdot}5X^0_H}{n_0 + 1};$$

$$p^0_{H_2O} = 0{\cdot}5X^0_H - p^0_{H_2};$$

$$p^0_{CO} = \frac{X^0_C}{1 + Kn_0};$$

$$p^0_{CO_2} = X^0_C - p^0_{CO}.$$

The numerical values of the equilibrium constant K for the chosen temperatures are determined from Table 2 in the Appendix.

The relative concentrations of the components of the undissociated combustion products is independent of the magnitude of the pressure. For a variation in the pressure p^0, the partial pressures of the gases (combustion products) are changed proportionally to this variation such that their sum remains equal to p^0. The relative partial pressures of the combustion products, or their molar fractions [see equation (1.3)], as a result of this are not changed. Dividing the right- and left-hand sides of equation (1.19) by p^0 and denoting the relative partial pressure of the ith component by $\bar{p}^0_i = p^0_i/p^0$, we obtain

$$\left.\begin{aligned} K &= \frac{\bar{p}^0_{CO_2}\bar{p}^0_{H_2}}{\bar{p}^0_{CO}\bar{p}^0_{H_2O}}; \\ \mu^0 A_O &= 2\bar{p}^0_{CO_2} + \bar{p}^0_{CO} + \bar{p}^0_{H_2O}; \\ \mu^0 A_C &= \bar{p}^0_{CO_2} + \bar{p}^0_{CO}; \\ \mu^0 A_H &= 2\bar{p}^0_{H_2O} + 2\bar{p}^0_{H_2}; \\ \mu^0 A_N &= 2\bar{p}^0_{N_2}. \end{aligned}\right\} \quad (1.21)$$

From a consideration of the equations of the system (1.21) it can be concluded that the relative partial pressures of the undissociated combustion products are independent of the magnitude of the overall pressure of these products p^0. The relative partial pressure of diatomic nitrogen depends neither on the pressure nor on the temperature of the combustion products.

For comparatively low temperatures of the combustion products (below 1800°K), dissociation processes do not, in practice, take place. The composition of the combustion products varies with change of temperature only in accordance with the laws of equilibrium for the water gas formation reaction. Consequently, equation (1.20) is completely applicable also for calculating the actual composition of the combustion products at temperatures not exceeding approximately 1800°K.

2. Relationship between the enthalpy of the undissociated combustion products and their temperature

The enthalpy of 1 kg of undissociated combustion products of the fuels under consideration is, in the general case, determined according to equation (1.18a). We add to the right-hand side of equation (1.18a) and subtract from it the terms

$$\frac{I_{CO}p^0_{CO_2}}{p^0\mu^0} \text{ and } \frac{I_{H_2}p^0_{H_2O}}{p^0\mu^0}.$$

Further, as a result of joint consideration of equations (1.11), (1.12), (1.10) and (1.15) we obtain

$$p^0_{CO_2} = p^0\mu^0 (A_O - A_C) - p^0_{H_2O}. \tag{1.22}$$

And, finally, using (1.10), (1.12)–(1.16), (1.18*a*) and (1.22) we find

$$i^0 = -(I_{CO} - I_{CO_2})(A_O - A_C) + \frac{1}{\mu^0}(I_{CO} - I_{CO_2} - I_{H_2} + $$

$$+ I_{H_2O})\frac{p^0_{H_2O}}{p^0} + I_{CO}A_C + 0{\cdot}5\, I_{H_2}A_H + 0{\cdot}5\, I_{N_2}A_{N_2}. \tag{1.23}$$

The aim of the present section is to find an approximate, but sufficiently accurate, relationship between the enthalpy and temperature of the undissociated combustion product in the case of unchanged elementary chemical composition of the fuel (for constant values of A_O, A_C, A_H, A_N and μ^0).

This relationship is determined by the dependence on temperature of the enthalpy or the algebraic sum of the enthalpies of the following components of the combustion products:

$$\left.\begin{aligned} &I_{CO} - I_{CO_2};\\ &I_{CO} - I_{CO_2} - I_{H_2} + I_{H_2O};\\ &I_{CO};\\ &I_{H_2};\\ &I_{N_2}, \end{aligned}\right\} \tag{1.24}$$

and also the quantity $p^0_{H_2O}/p^0$.

The range of temperatures of the combustion products of rocket fuels is limited to their temperatures in the combustion chamber and in the discharge section of the nozzle. For a pressure in the combustion chamber of 20–100 atm for the combustion products, the temperature is usually equal to 2500 to 4000°K, and for the most part lies within the limits 2800–3800°K.* The temperature of the combustion products in the discharge section of the nozzle at a pressure of 0·5–1·5 atm in the overwhelming majority of cases is found within the limits 1400–2800°K. Consequently, the sought-for law of variation of enthalpy of the combustion products should be accurate in the first place for a temperature range limited by the values 1400 and 3800°K.

Figure 1 depicts graphically the relationship between the values of the parameters (1.24) and the absolute temperature (continuous lines). The values of the enthalpy of the components of the combustion products (denoted on the graph by circles) are taken from Table 1 in the Appendix. It can be seen that the relationship between the parameters in (1.24) and the temperature in the temperature region of 1400–3800°K is close to linear. However, to obtain a simplified but sufficiently accurate single analytical relationship between the parameters in (1.24) and the temperature over the entire temperature range of 1400–3800°K was found to be impossible. Therefore, the range of temperatures considered is divided into two regions:

1400 – 2800 °K (Region *L*)

2800 – 3800 °K (Region *H*)

The temperature 2800°K was chosen as the dividing line as it comes approximately in the middle of the range under consideration and in the vast majority of cases it divides the temperatures of the combustion products in the combustion chamber of a rocket engine from the temperatures in the discharge section of the nozzle.

For each one of these parameters (1.24) we selected, in both temperature zones, a certain approximately linear function (broken line in Fig. 1) of the form

$$y = y_{2800} + b(T - 2800). \qquad (1.25)$$

Here y_{2800} is the values of the parameters in (1.24) at a temperature of 2800°K. The values of the coefficients b for the parameters in (1.24) were determined by a graphical method.

* Bearing in mind fuel of the type under consideration.

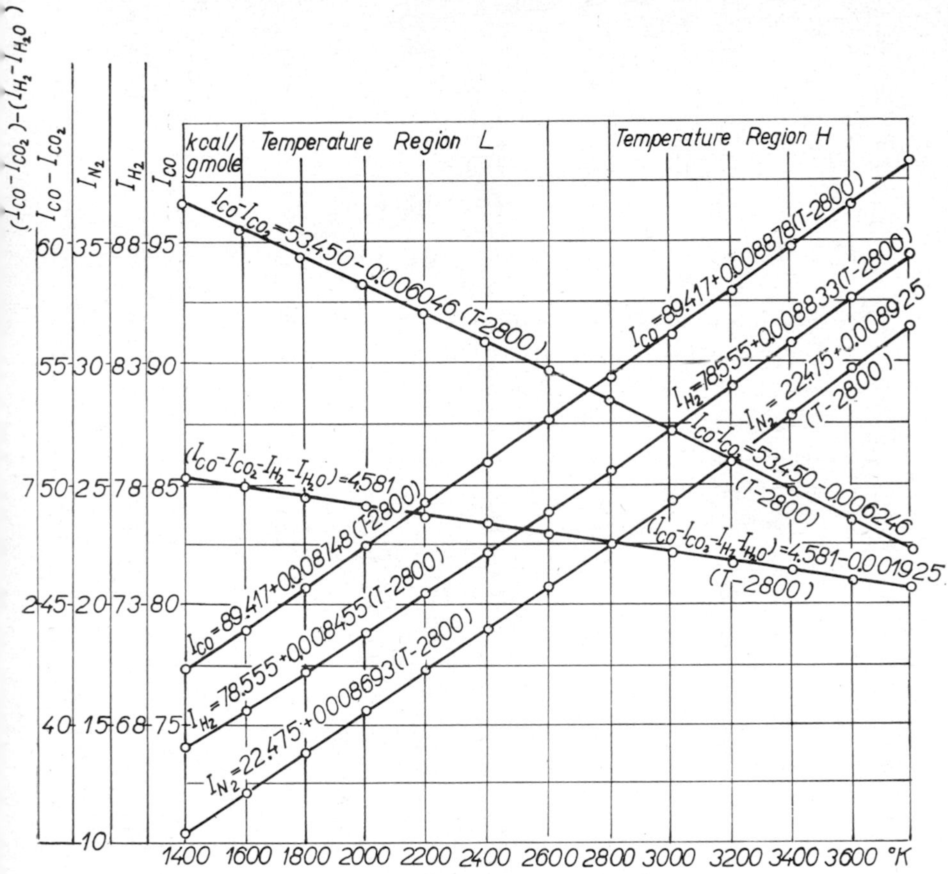

FIG. 1

The undeveloped functions of (1.25) have the following form (enthalpy in kcal/mole).

Temperature region H:

$$\left.\begin{aligned} I_{CO} &= 89{\cdot}417 + 0{\cdot}008878\,(T - 2800); \\ I_{H_2} &= 78{\cdot}555 + 0{\cdot}008833\,(T - 2800); \\ I_{N_2} &= 22{\cdot}475 + 0{\cdot}008925\,(T - 2800); \\ I_{CO} - I_{CO_2} &= 53{\cdot}450 - 0{\cdot}006246\,(T - 2800); \\ I_{CO} - I_{CO_2} - I_{H_2} + I_{H_2O} &= 4{\cdot}581 - 0{\cdot}001925\,(T - 2800). \end{aligned}\right\} \quad (1{\cdot}26)$$

Temperature region L:

$$\left.\begin{aligned} I_{CO} &= 89{\cdot}417 + 0{\cdot}008748\,(T - 2800);\\ I_{H_2} &= 78{\cdot}555 + 0{\cdot}008455\,(T - 2800);\\ I_{N_2} &= 22{\cdot}475 + 0{\cdot}008693\,(T - 2800);\\ I_{CO} - I_{CO_2} &= 53{\cdot}450 - 0{\cdot}006046\,(T - 2800);\\ I_{CO} - I_{CO_2} - I_{H_2} + I_{H_2O} &= 4{\cdot}581 - 0{\cdot}001979\,(T - 2800). \end{aligned}\right\} \quad (1.27)$$

The maximum error in calculating the values of I_{CO}, I_{H_2}, I_{N_2} and $I_{CO} - I_{CO_2}$ according to equations (1.26) and (1.27) does not exceed 5 per cent. The maximum value of the error in the parameter $I_{CO} - I_{CO_2} - I_{H_2} + I_{H_2O}$ amounts to 1·5 per cent. Since however, for the case of the combustion products of all the fuels being considered the fractional term

$$\frac{1}{\mu^0}\left(I_{CO} - I_{CO_2} - I_{H_2} + I_{H_2O}\right)\frac{p^0_{H_2O}}{p^0}$$

in the sum of (1.23) is small, then the indicated error for this parameter will not give a significant error in determining the enthalpy i^0.

Solving concurrently equations (1.23) and (1.26) we find the relationship between the enthalpy i^0_H and the temperature of the combustion products in the case of temperature region H (2800–3800 °K):

$$\begin{aligned} i^0_H = {} & [142{\cdot}867 + 0{\cdot}002632\,(T - 2800)]\,A_C + \\ & + [39{\cdot}278 + 0{\cdot}004417\,(T - 2800)]\,A_H + \\ & + [11{\cdot}238 + 0{\cdot}004463\,(T - 2800)]\,A_N - \\ & - [53{\cdot}450 - 0{\cdot}006246\,(T - 2800)]\,A_O + \\ & + \frac{1}{\mu^0}[4{\cdot}581 - 0{\cdot}001925\,(T - 2800)]\frac{p^0_{H_2O}}{p^0}. \end{aligned} \quad (1.28)$$

Here, the dimensions of the numerical coefficients are kcal/mole, kcal/mole·deg and °K. The dimensions of i^0_H are kcal/kg.

It is not possible to use equation (1.28) directly to determine i^0_H, since the dependence of the parameter $p^0_{H_2O}/p^0$ on the temperature is not known. In order to simplify the form of the equation we shall use the example described further.

We find the specific heat of the combustion products at constant pressure, equal to the derivative of the enthalpy with respect to temperature (for a fixed elementary chemical composition of the combustion products):

$$c^0_{p\cdot H} = \frac{di^0_H}{dT} = 0{\cdot}002632\, A_C + 0{\cdot}004417\, A_H + \\ + 0{\cdot}004463\, A_N + 0{\cdot}006246\, A_O + \\ + \frac{1}{\mu^0}[4{\cdot}581 - 0{\cdot}001925\,(T - 2800)]\, d\left(\frac{p^0_{H_2O}/p^0}{dT}\right) - 0{\cdot}001925\,\frac{p^0_{H_2O}}{\mu^0 p^0}. \qquad (1.29)$$

An estimate of the specific gravity of the two latter component sums reveals the following. The fractional term

$$\frac{1}{\mu^0}[4.581 - 0.001925\, T - 2800)]\, d\left(\frac{p^0_{H_2O}/p^0}{dT}\right)$$

does not exceed 0·1 per cent of the value of $c^0_{p,\,H}$, consequently this term can be neglected. The fractional term $0{\cdot}001925\; p^0_{H_2O}/p^0\,\mu^0$ attains 10–15 per cent of the value of $c^0_{p,H}$, therefore it is not possible to neglect this term. It is possible to simplify this expression considerably. The partial pressure of the water vapour in the undissociated combustion products is only very slightly changed with change of temperature. Even in very unfavourable circumstances (for the combustion products of fuels with small hydrogen and oxygen content) the variation of the partial pressure of the water vapour amounts to about 5 per cent of its value for a change in temperature from 3800 to 2800 °K.

According to these considerations, taking into account that the fractional term $0{\cdot}001925\; p^0_{H_2O}/p^0\,\mu^0$ is nevertheless small, we have made the assumption that in the given case, in place of the partial pressure of water $p^0_{H_2O}$ independent of the temperature assumed for the calculation of $c^0_{p,\,H}$, the parameter $p^0_{H_2O,\,2800}$ can be used — the partial pressure of water vapour at a temperature of 2800 °K:

$$p^0_{H_2O,\,2800} \cong p^0_{H_2O}. \qquad (1.30)$$

As a result of this supposition, as calculations for actual fuels show, the error in determining the value of $c^0_{p,\,H}$ does not exceed 0·1 per cent. For the calculations below this is permissible.

As a result of neglecting the term $1/\mu^0\,[4{\cdot}581 - 0{\cdot}001925\,(T - 2800)]\,\frac{d(p^0_{H_2O}/p^0)}{dT}$ a somewhat less value of $c^0_{p,\,H}$ is obtained. Using $p^0_{H_2O,\,2800}/p^0\;\mu^0$ in place of $p^0_{H_2O}/p^0\,\mu^0$ leads to some increase in the value of $c^0_{p,\,H}$. As a result, a partial mutual compensation of both errors occurs.

The relative partial pressure of the water vapour in the undissociated combustion products of the fuels being considered, at a temperature of 2800 °K, can be calculated with sufficient accuracy by the formula

$$\frac{p^0_{H_2O\,2800}}{p^0\mu^0} = [0{\cdot}612 + 0{\cdot}415\log(\alpha - 0{\cdot}42)]\,A_H. \qquad (1.31)$$

Formula (1.31) is found as a result of processing the direct calculations of the chemical composition of the undissociated combustion products. It gives a sufficiently accurate relationship between the relative partial pressures of water vapour at 2800 °K and the elementary composition of the fuel.

The simplifications made lead to an insignificant increase in the value of $c^0_{p,H}$, determined by the approximate formula, in comparison with its value obtained by direct calculation. This was shown by comparison of the results of the corresponding calculations for the case of a number of fuels. For compensation, the error on the right-hand side of expression (1.29) should be multiplied by a correction factor, less than unity. According to our comparison calculations, the correction factor is equal to 0·997. Finally, we obtain

$$c^0_{p,H} = \{2{\cdot}624\,A_C + 4{\cdot}450\,A_H + 6{\cdot}227\,A_O + \\ + [3{\cdot}229 - 0{\cdot}797\log(\alpha - 0{\cdot}42)]\,A_H\}\,10^{-3}. \qquad (1.32)$$

In order to assess the accuracy of formula (1.32) a comparison is carried out of the values of $c^0_{p,H}$ obtained by direct calculation and according to the formula given, for elementary chemical compositions differing greatly between themselves. The results of the calculations on comparison show that the error in the magnitude of $c^0_{p,H}$, calculated according to formula (1.32) does not exceed 0·6 per cent (Table 1).

Let us establish the same relationship as (1.32) for the temperature region L (1400–2800 °K). By simultaneous solution of equations (1.23) and (1.27) we find the expression which enables the value of the enthalpy of the undissociated combustion products in the temperature region L to be calculated:

$$i^0_L = [142{\cdot}867 + 0{\cdot}002702\,(T - 2800)]\,A_C + \\ + [39{\cdot}278 + 0{\cdot}004228\,(T - 2800)]\,A_H + \\ + [11{\cdot}238 + 0{\cdot}004347\,(T - 2800)]\,A_N - \\ - [53{\cdot}450 - 0{\cdot}006046\,(T - 2800)]\,A_O + \\ + \frac{1}{\mu^0}[4{\cdot}581 - 0{\cdot}001979\,(T - 2800)]\,\frac{p^0_{H_2O}}{p^0}. \qquad (1.33)$$

Direct application of equation (1.33) for determining i_L^0 is impossible, since the dependence of $p^0_{H_2O}/p^0$ on temperature is not known.

The specific heat at constant pressure of the combustion products $c^0_{p,L}$ is equal to the derivative of the enthalpy with respect to temperature (for constant elementary chemical composition of the combustion products):

$$c^0_{p,L} = \frac{di^0_L}{dT} = 0{\cdot}002702\, A_C + 0{\cdot}004228\, A_H + 0{\cdot}004347\, A_N + $$
$$+ 0{\cdot}006046\, A_0 + \frac{1}{\mu^0}[4{\cdot}581 - 0{\cdot}001979\,(T - 2800)] \times$$
$$\times \frac{d\,(p^0_{H_2O}/p^0)}{dT} - 0{\cdot}001979\, \frac{p^0_{H_2O}}{p^0\, \mu^0}. \qquad (1.34)$$

TABLE 1

Arbitrary number of chemical composition	$\frac{A_C}{A_H}$	$\frac{A_N}{A_H}$	A_H	$a = 0{\cdot}90$		
				$c_{p,H}$ determined by direct calculation	$c^0_{p,H}$ calculated by formula (1.32)	Error in value of $c^0_{p,H}$ %
1	0·5	8	7·116	0·3468	0·3471	0·086
2	0·1333	1·4	30·10	0·4323	0·4321	0·023
3	0·077	0·385	59·83	0·5440	0·5422	0·331
4	0·05556	0	95·60	0·6780	0·6741	0·575
5	1·75	5·5	6·382	0·3506	0·3508	0·057
9	3·125	2·75	5·707	0·3525	0·3525	0
11	0·8333	0	23·68	0·4224	0·4218	0·142
14	1·5	0	14·41	0·3902	0·3896	0·154
15	4·5	0	5·215	0·3580	0·3573	0·195

Arbitrary number of chemical composition	$\frac{A_C}{A_H}$	$\frac{A_N}{A_H}$	A_H	$a = 0{\cdot}90$		
				$C^0_{p,H}$ determined by direct calculation	$C^0_{p,H}$ calculated by formula (1.32)	Error in value of $C^0_{p,H}$ %
1_3	0·5	8	7·500	0·3468	0·3475	0·202
2_3	0·1333	1·4	33·83	0·4485	0·4489	0·089
3_3	0·077	0·385	73·63	0·6022	0·6021	0·016
4_3	0·05556	0	132·8	0·8300	0·8302	0·024
5_3	1·75	5·5	7·280	0·3483	0·3483	0
9_3	3·125	2·75	7·004	0·3480	0·3458	0·632
11_3	0·8333	0	31·47	0·4454	0·4438	0·359

We shall evaluate the specific effect of the last two terms of the right-hand side of equation (1.34). Analysis of the results of these calculations, with this objective, shows that the fractional term

$$1/\mu_0\,[4{\cdot}581 - 0{\cdot}001979\,(T - 2800)]\;\mathrm{d}\left(\frac{p^0_{\mathrm{H_2O}}/p^0}{\mathrm{d}T}\right)$$

does not exceed 0·6 per cent of the value of $c^0_{p,\,\mathrm{L}}$, and therefore we shall neglect it. The fractional term $0{\cdot}001979\ p^0_{\mathrm{H_2O}}/p^0\,\mu^0$ amounts to 10 per cent of the value of $c^0_{p,\,\mathrm{L}}$, and it is obviously impossible to neglect this term for calculating $c^0_{\mathrm{H_2O}}$. However, this determination can be simplified without significantly reducing the accuracy of the results of the calculation. For this, the value of the parameter $p^0_{\mathrm{H_2O}}/p^0\,\mu^0$ taken at a certain temperature, we shall substitute (as in region "*H*") by its value at a temperature of 2800 °K — $p^0_{\mathrm{H_2O},\ 2800}/p^0\,\mu^0$. The parameter $p^0_{\mathrm{H_2O},\,2800}/p^0\,\mu^0$ is determined according to formula (1.31).

The assumptions mentioned lead to a certain reduction in the value of $c^0_{p,\,\mathrm{L}}$, and therefore in order to determine $c^0_{p,\,\mathrm{L}}$ by an approximation method, the right-hand side of expression (1.34) should be multiplied by a constant correction factor, numerically greater than unity. Comparative calculations carried out by us lead to a value for this correction factor equal to 1·005.

Consequently, having carried out the simplification of equation (1.34) as mentioned, we find

$$c^0_{p\mathrm{L}} = \{2.716\,A_{\mathrm{C}} + 4.369\,A_{\mathrm{N}} + 6.076\,A_{\mathrm{O}} + \\ + [3.032 - 0.825\log(\alpha - 0.42)]\,A_{\mathrm{H}}\}\cdot 10^{-3} \qquad (1.35)$$

The error in the value of $c^0_{p,\,\mathrm{L}}$ obtained by the approximate expression (1.35), for combustion products of a number of elementary chemical compositions differing strongly amongst themselves, does not exceed 1 per cent. The results of the comparative calculations are presented in Table 2.

Expressions (1.32) and (1.35) define the derivative of the enthalpy of 1 kg of combustion products at the temperature of the respective temperature regions. Integrating this equation we find the enthalpy of 1 kg undissociated combustion products in the corresponding temperature regions.

For temperature region *H*

$$i^0_H - i^0_{2800} = \int_{2800}^{T} c^0_{p,H}\,\mathrm{d}T\,.$$

TABLE 2

$a = 0{\cdot}90$

Arbitrary number of chemical composition	$\frac{A_C}{A_H}$	$\frac{A_N}{A_H}$	A_H	$c^0_{p\,H}$ determined by direct calculation	$c^0_{p,H}$ calculated by formula (1.35)	Error in value of $c^0_{p,H}$ %
1	0·5	8	7·116	0·3421	0·3400	0·61
2	0·1333	1·4	30·10	0·4258	0·4203	1·29
5	1·75	5·5	6·382	0·3464	0·3444	0·57
6	0·7	1·6	16·91	0·3846	0·3817	0·75
9	3·125	2·75	5·707	0·3482	0·3465	0·48
10	1·25	0·5	15·11	0·3844	0·3818	0·67
11	0·8333	0	23·68	0·4161	0·4122	0·93
12	3·75	1·5	5·490	0·3512	0·3501	0·31
13	2·14	0·428	9·840	0·3683	0·3657	0·70
14	1·5	0	14·41	0·3844	0·3820	0·57
15	4·5	0	5·215	0·3538	0·3518	0·56

Since the parameter $c^0_{p,\,H}$ is independent of the temperature, then we finally obtain

$$i^0_H = i^0_{2800} + c^0_{p,\,H}\,(T - 2800)\,. \qquad (1.36)$$

Similarly, for the temperature zone L

$$i^0_L = i^0_{2800} + c^0_{p,\,L}\,(T - 2800)\,. \qquad (1.37)$$

The parameter i^0_{2800} entering into equations (1.36) and (1.37) represents the enthalpy of the undissociated combustion products of the fuels at a temperature of 2800 °K. In order to calculate i^0_{H} and i^0_{L} according to expressions (1.36) and (1.37) it is necessary to know the value of the enthalpy i^0_{2800}.

The method of calculating the value of the enthalpies of the undissociated combustion products is given in the next section.

3. Enthalpy of Undissociated Combustion Products

Equations (1.32) and (1.35) enable the values of the parameters $c^0_{p,\,\mathrm{H}}$ and $c^0_{p,\,\mathrm{L}}$ to be calculated without preliminary calculation of the chemical composition of the undissociated combustion products. For this, it is sufficient to know only the initial elementary chemical composition of the fuel, defined by the values of A_{C}, A_{H}, A_{N}, A_{O}.

Consequently, except for the term i^0_{2800}, no other terms enter into the right-hand side of equations (1.36) and (1.37), required for calculating both values of the preliminary calculation of the chemical composition of the combustion products.

In order to determine i^0_{2800} it is necessary, in the general case, to carry out a calculation of the chemical composition of the combustion products at a temperature of 2800 °K. Thus, in order to calculate also the values of the enthalpy at other temperatures according to equations (1.36) and (1.37) it is necessary to carry out a preliminary calculation of the chemical composition of the combustion products at a temperature of 2800 °K. The latter circumstance makes the use of equations (1.36) and (1.37) noticeably more difficult for calculating the enthalpies of the undissociated combustion products. It is desirable to simplify the calculation of the parameter i^0_{2800} as much as possible.

Simplification of the method of calculating the parameter i^0_{2800}, and thereby i^0_H and i^0_L, comprises the contents of the present section.

The enthalpy of the undissociated combustion products at a temperature of 2800 °K, as also at any other temperature, is calculated according to equation (1.18a). In the general case it is a function of the following parameters:

$$i^0 = f(A_C, A_H, A_N, A_O, T).$$

As a result of considering the enthalpy i^0 at fixed temperature of the combustion products ($T = \text{const}$), the number of parameters is reduced by one. Thus, for example, for $T = 2800$ °K, we have

$$i^0_{2800} = f(A_C, A_H, A_N, A_O).$$

In this case the enthalpy of the undissociated combustion products depends only on the initial elementary chemical composition of the fuel. The number of g-atoms of one of the chemical elements for known numbers of g-atoms of the other three elements (and the known atomic weights of all four elements) can be found, as the complement of the weight of fuel for 1 kg. Thus, the number of parameters upon which i^0_{2800} depends is reduced to three in consequence of the exclusion, for example, of the parameter A_N.

The number of gram-atoms of oxygen A_O can be expressed via the parameters A_H, A_C and a in accordance with the formula

$$a = \frac{A_O}{2\,A_C + 0{\cdot}5\,A_H}\,.$$

Finally we obtain

$$i^0_{2800} = f(A_C, A_H, \alpha). \tag{1.38}$$

The carbon and hydrogen content of fuels for rocket engines fluctuates within wide limits. It is otherwise with the excess oxygen factor α. The operating range for excess of oxygen, with which rocket engines function, is relatively small. We shall consider the operation of an engine for an excess oxygen factor having values of 0·5 to 1·0. Within this same range of values for the excess oxygen factor the theoretical study of the characteristics of fuel combustion and operation of the engine is usually carried out. For this it is sufficient to carry out thermal calculations for certain values of α and further, by graphical interpolation methods, to determine the required characteristics for all intermediate values of α.

Taking into account what has been said above, the problem concerning the determination of the parameter i^0_{2800} assumes real significance. We shall assign values to the excess oxygen factor α of 0·95; 0·90; 0·80; 0·70; 0·60 and 0·55. For each one of these values, the enthalpy $i^0_{2\ 00}$ is designated by functions of only two parameters: A_C and A_H.

It presents an advantage to carry out direct calculations for every fixed value of α by determining the dependence of the enthalpy i^0_{2800} on the parameters A_C and A_H and to construct the corresponding nomograms. According to a number of considerations, the significance of which will be clarified after reading subsequent chapters of the book, we choose as independent variables for constructing the nomograms not the parameters A_C and A_H, but the parameters X^0_C and X^0_H, connected with A_C and A_H in the following manner:

$$X^0_C = 40\,\mu^0\,A_C; \tag{1.39}$$

$$X^0_H = 40\,\mu^0\,A_H. \tag{1.40}$$

In these nomograms, as the sought-for function, there figures not the value of i^0_{2800} — the enthalpy of the undissociated combustion products at a temperature of 2800 °K, but the quantity i^0_v, connected with i^0_{2800} by the expression

$$i^0_v = 40\,\mu^0\,i^0_{2800}. \tag{1.41}$$

Nomograms have been constructed for the excess oxygen factors enumerated above and they are presented in Figs. 1–6 of the Appendix.

In order to relate the supporting points for constructing the nomograms, the results are used of the directly calculated values of the parameter i_v^0 for combustion products with chemical compositions as presented in Table 3.

The limits of variation of the values of the parameters X_C^0, X_H^0 and α in Table 3 correspond to the limit of variation of the percentage

TABLE 3

Arbitrary number of chemical composition	X_C^0	X_H^0	X_N^0	α = 0·95 X_O^0	0·90 X_O^0	0·80 X_O^0	0·70 X_O^0	0·60 X_O^0	0·55 X_O^0
1	4	8	64	11·4	10·8	9·6	8·4	7·2	6·6
2	4	30	42	21·85	20·7	18·4	16·1	13·8	12·65
3	4	52	20	32·3	30·6	27·2	23·8	20·4	18·7
4	4	72	0	41·8	39·6	35·2	30·8	26·4	24·2
5	14	8	44	30·4	28·8	25·6	22·4	19·2	17·6
6	14	20	32	36·1	34·2	30·4	26·6	22·8	20·9
7	14	40	12	45·6	43·2	38·4	33·6	28·8	26·4
8	14	52	0	51·3	48·6	43·2	37·8	32·4	29·7
9	25	8	22	51·3	48·6	43·2	37·8	32·4	29·7
10	25	20	10	57·0	54·0	48·0	42·0	36·0	33·0
11	25	30	0	61·75	58·5	52·0	45·5	39·0	35·75
12	30	8	12	60·8	57·6	51·2	44·8	38·4	35·2
13	30	14	6	63·65	60·3	53·6	46·9	40·2	36·85
14	30	20	0	66·5	63·0	56·0	49·0	42·0	38·5
15	36	8	0	72·2	68·4	60·8	53·2	45·0	41·2

Note. The arbitrary composition number, written without suffix (column 1) corresponds to a value for $\alpha = 0{\cdot}90$ (column 6). For other values of the excess oxygen factor α, the suffix 0, 1, 2, 3 or 4 is written below and to the right of the arbitrary composition number. For example, for composition No. 4:

α	Arbitrary composition number
0·95	4_0
0·90	4
0·80	4_1
0·70	4_2
0·60	4_3
0·55	4_4

Other compositions are numbered similarly.

composition of the chemical elements in the fuel, as mentioned in the foreword to this book. The compositions, designated in Tables 1, 2 and 3 by one and the same arbitrary number, are similarly independent of the fact that they are expressed via any of the parameters (via A_C, A_H, A_N, A_O or X_C^0, X_H^0, X_N^0, X_O^0). The calculation of the parameter i_v^0 is carried out by the usual method, using the table of enthalpies of the combustion products given in the Appendix.

The sought-for value of i_{2800}^0 is determined by the nomograms in the following manner. We shall assume that it is required to determine the value of i_{2800} for a certain fixed value of the excess oxygen factor $\alpha = \text{const}$ (corresponding with one of the values of α on which the nomograms are constructed) for a fuel, the chemical composition of which is known. For this, the values of the independent variables X_C^0 and X_H^0 are calculated according to formulae (1.39) and (1.40).

Then, from the point on the abscissa axis, corresponding to the value of X_H^0, a straight line parallel to the ordinate axis is drawn to the intersection with the line corresponding to the value of X_C^0. The ordinate of the point of intersection determines the value of i_v^0. The sought-for enthalpy i_{2800}^0 is found according to expression (1.41):

$$i_{2800}^0 = \frac{i_v^0}{40\,\mu^0}.$$

In the case when the given value of the excess oxygen factor α does not agree with one of the values of this coefficient, for which the nomograms are plotted, but does not exceed the limits $0{\cdot}55 \leqslant \alpha \leqslant 0{\cdot}95$, in order to determine the value of the parameter i_{2800}^0 for a given α it is necessary to determine in succession the value of this parameter with the aid of nomograms constructed for values of α close to that given and, having constructed a supplementary graph with coordinates (i_{2800}^0; α) to find the value of i_{2800}^0.

Thus, the nomograms given in Figs. 1–6 of the Appendix make it possible to determine the parameter i_{2800}^0 without a preliminary calculation of the chemical composition of the combustion products.

Since the independent parameters X_C^0 and X_H^0 are used for determining the value of i_{2800}^0, it is more convenient to carry out a calculation of the values $c_{p,H}^0$ and $c_{p,L}^0$ via these parameters and not via A_C and A_H.

Transforming expressions (1.32) and (1.35) we obtain:

$$c^0_{p,H} = \frac{1}{40\,\mu^0}[356{\cdot}0 + (12{\cdot}454\,a - 6{\cdot}276)\,X^0_C + + (3{\cdot}114\,a - 1{\cdot}221)\,X^0_H - 0{\cdot}797 \log(a - 0{\cdot}42)\,X^0_H]\,10^{-3}; \quad (1.42)$$

$$c^0_{p,L} = \frac{1}{40\,\mu^0}[349{\cdot}6 + (12{\cdot}152\,a - 6{\cdot}022)\,X^0_C + + (3{\cdot}038\,a - 1{\cdot}336)\,X^0_H - 0{\cdot}825 \log(a - 0{\cdot}42)\,X^0_H]\,10^{-3}. \quad (1.43)$$

In order to assess the error in the values for i^0_H and i^0_H, comparative calculations have been carried out by us of the values of the parameters for the combustion products of a number of chemical compositions differing widely amongst themselves. The values of i^0_H and i^0_L were calculated by the direct method and according to expressions (1.36) and (1.37).

The results of the calculations are presented in Table 4.

TABLE 4

Arbitrary number of chemical composition	Temperature of combustion products, $T°$ K	Value of i^0_H or i^0_L according to equations (1.36) or (1.37), kcal/kg	Value of i^0_H or i^0_L as a result of calculation by direct method kcal/kg	Error in determining i^0_H or i^0_L kcal/kg	Error in determining i^0_H or i^0_L in % of i^0_H or i^0_L
1	3800	1279·0	1283·0	4·0	0·31
1	3400	1140·2	1136·0	4·2	0·37
1	3000	1001·4	998·0	3·4	0·34
4	3800	2579·0	2584·0	5·0	0·19
4	3400	2309·4	2310·0	0·6	0·03
4	3000	2039·8	2038·0	1·8	0·09
5	3400	1236·6	1238·0	1·4	0·11
5	2400	888·4	888·5	0·1	0·01
8	3400	1872·2	1876·0	3·8	0·20
8	2400	1356·6	1356·0	0·6	0·04
9	3400	1321·8	1327·0	5·2	0·39
9	2400	971·6	975·0	3·4	0·35
11	3400	1584·2	1586·0	1·8	0·11
11	2400	1166·2	1167·0	0·8	0·07
15	3400	1400·2	1400·0	0·2	0·01
15	3000	1257·4	1256·0	1·4	0·11
15	2400	1045·2	1044·0	1·2	0·11

It follows from an analysis of this table that in the cases of combustion products of the composition under consideration the error in the magnitudes of i^0_H and i^0_L, calculated according to equations (1.36) and (1.37) does not exceed 0·4 per cent.

CHAPTER 2

Thermodynamic Parameters of Dissociated Products of Combustion

4. Dissociated Combustion Products

The high temperature of combustion of fuels in rocket motors gives rise to dissociation of individual components of the combustion products, as a result of which more complex molecules are decomposed into simpler molecules and mono-atomic particles. Dissociation reactions are accompanied by the absorption of heat and an increase in the chemical energy of the combustion products. The heat absorption resulting from the combustion products is a factor which limits the magnitude of the maximum attainable combustion temperature of a given fuel and the degree of dissociation is determined by the magnitude of the temperature.

The formation, as a result of dissociation, of lighter mono- and diatomic gases — the products of dissociation — leads to a reduction of the mean ("apparent") molecular weight of the gaseous combustion products. If we consider dissociation taking place at constant pressure, then it is accompanied by an increase in volume of the combustion products. Dissociation, taking place at constant volume, causes an increase in the pressure of the combustion products.

As a result of the significant increase of pressure of the combustion products (theoretically for $p \to \infty$), all the reactions can be assigned which take place together with an increase in the number of moles and which give rise to combining reactions of the previously dissociated molecules and atoms. These reactions are called recombination reactions. The phenomenon of recombination will also occur as a result of a reduction in the temperature of the combustion products.

In the general case the composition of the combustion products depends on the initial chemical composition of the fuel, the pressure and the temperature. Calculations show that in the combustion products of the rocket fuels being considered, 11 components are contained in noticeable quantities: CO_2, CO, H_2O, H_2, N_2, O_2, OH, H, O, N and NO.

The formation of these components is a consequence of six dissociation reactions and an oxidation reaction of diatomic nitrogen:

$$\left.\begin{aligned} &CO_2 \rightleftarrows CO + \frac{1}{2} O_2; \\ &H_2O \rightleftarrows H_2 + \frac{1}{2} O_2; \\ &H_2O \rightleftarrows OH + \frac{1}{2} H_2; \\ &\frac{1}{2} H_2 \rightleftarrows H; \\ &\frac{1}{2} O_2 \rightleftarrows O; \\ &\frac{1}{2} N_2 \rightleftarrows N; \\ &\frac{1}{2} N_2 + \frac{1}{2} O_2 \rightleftarrows NO. \end{aligned}\right\} \qquad (2.1)$$

In order to calculate the actual temperature of combustion of the fuel, i.e. the temperature at which dissociation of the combustion products commences, and also the partial pressures of these products, it is necessary to assemble a system of equations such that the total number of equations should be equal to the number of unknown quantities. If the dissociation process be considered as a process which takes place without change of volume of the combustion products, then as a result of the increase in the number of moles, dependent upon the dissociation, the pressure is increased and becomes greater than the pressure of the combustion products calculated without taking dissociation into account.

As a result of this, the approach to the solution of the problem of determining the characteristics of the combustion products under dissociation conditions is carried out in two stages. In the first stage the simpler problem is solved of determining the characteristics of the combustion products without taking into account dissociation and the results so obtained are considered as a first approximation to the actual case. In the second stage, the errors to the resulting parameters of the first approximation are considered, which enable an accurate solution to be obtained. Transition from the results of the first approximation to the accurate values of the parameters is carried out for constant volume and temperature of the combustion products.

In order to solve the problem it is necessary to determine 13 unknown quantities, namely 11 partial pressures of the combustion products and also the temperature and volume of the mixture of these products. Consequently, the system should comprise not less than 13 equations. As the first seven equations the equilibrium constants of the reactions in (2.1) are used:

$$\frac{p_{CO}\sqrt{p_{O_2}}}{p_{CO_2}} = K_1 = f_1(T);$$

$$\frac{p_{H_2}\sqrt{p_{O_2}}}{p_{H_2O}} = K_2 = f_2(T);$$

$$\frac{p_{OH}\sqrt{p_{H_2}}}{p_{H_2O}} = K_3 = f_3(T);$$

$$\frac{p_{H}}{\sqrt{p_{H_2}}} = K_4 = f_4(T);$$

$$\frac{p_{O}}{\sqrt{p_{O_2}}} = K_5 = f_5(T);$$

$$\frac{p_{N}}{\sqrt{p_{N_2}}} = K_6 = f_6(T);$$

$$\frac{p_{NO}}{\sqrt{p_{N_2}}\sqrt{p_{O_2}}} = K_7 = f_7(T).$$

Usually, the value of the equilibrium constants of the combustion products from the fuels being considered are given by tables in which the values of the temperature are given in multiples of hundreds of degrees centigrade with intervals within 100–200°. In this book the values of the equilibrium constants given in the Appendix are used. It should be noted that the values of the equilibrium constants are given with continuously increasing accuracy and therefore, in other works tables may be encountered with somewhat different values for the same equilibrium constants.

For further solution of the problem the equations of material balance are utilized.

The equations of material balance for the case of combustion of a fuel, taking into account dissociation of the combustion products, are obtained similarly to equations (1.11)–(1.14), effective for the undissociated combustion products. Let us derive, for example, the material balance equation for the chemical element oxygen. In 1 kg of fuel there are contained A_0 g-atoms of oxygen. A number of the combustion products also contain oxygen, namely: in every mole of CO_2 and O_2 are contained 2 g-atoms, and in every mole of CO,

H_2O, O, OH and NO there is 1 g-atom of oxygen. In accordance with the Law of Conservation of Mass the number of g-atoms of oxygen in the combustion products should be equal to their quantity in the fuel. Consequently

$$A_O = 2M_{CO_2} + 2M_{O_2} + M_{CO} + M_{H_2O} + M_O + M_{OH} + M_{NO}.$$

We shall transform the latter expression. We multiply the right- and left-hand sides by $p\mu$ and the product of the parameters of the left-hand side we denote by the symbol X_0:

$$X_0 = p\mu\, A_0 \tag{2.2}$$

Here p is the pressure of the dissociated combustion products, μ is a parameter, depending on μ_k — the "apparent" molecular weight of the dissociated combustion products and defined by the formula

$$\mu = \frac{\mu_k}{1000} \tag{2.3}$$

By analogy with (1.6), the joint sum of the right-hand side is written down via the partial pressures, since for every component of the combustion products the equation is found to hold good:

$$p_i = p\mu\, M_i \tag{2.4}$$

The equation of balance for oxygen is obtained in the form

$$X_O = 2p_{CO_2} + 2p_{O_2} + p_{CO} + p_{H_2O} + p_O + p_{OH} + p_{NO} \tag{2.5}$$

Similarly, for the other three chemical elements

$$X_C = p_{CO_2} + p_{CO}; \tag{2.6}$$

$$X_H = 2p_{H_2O} + 2p_{H_2} + p_{OH} + p_H; \tag{2.7}$$

$$X_N = 2p_{N_2} + p_{NO} + p_N. \tag{2.8}$$

Here, by analogy with the parameter X_O, the symbols X_C, X_H and X_N denote

$$X_C = p\ \mu\ A_C \tag{2.9}$$

$$X_H = p\ \mu\ A_H \tag{2.10}$$

$$X_N = p\ \mu\ A_N \tag{2.11}$$

In order to solve the problem posed, it is necessary to compile two further equations, since there are 13 unknown values and there are only 11 equations so far.

In the absence of thermal losses, the enthalpy of the fuel is equal to the enthalpy of the combustion products, the composition of which corresponds to the combustion temperature T_c

$$i_T = i_{T_c}. \tag{2.12}$$

In order to solve equation (2.12) it is necessary to be able to determine the enthalpy of the combustion products with respect to the known composition of the combustion products for any specified temperature T. This enthalpy can be calculated by a formula similar to formula (1.18a):

$$i = \frac{1}{p\mu}(I_{CO_2}p_{CO_2} + I_{CO}p_{CO} + I_{H_2O}p_{H_2O} + I_{H_2}p_{H_2} +$$

$$+ I_{N_2}p_{N_2} + I_{OH}p_{OH} + I_{O_2}p_{O_2} + I_{NO}p_{NO} + I_O p_O + I_H p_H + I_N p_N). \tag{2.13}$$

Here I_{CO_2}, I_{CO}, etc., are the values of the enthalpies of the combustion products at a temperature T.

The last missing equation is determined by the method adopted by us of transition from the parameters of the dissociation products without change of volume and temperature. Consequently

$$v = v^0 \text{ (for } T = \text{constant)}. \tag{2.14}$$

The mixture of gaseous combustion products, the individual components of which may enter into chemical reactions between themselves, can be considered as an ideal gas obeying the equation of state. We shall write it down separately for the case of undissociated and dissociated combustion products:

$$v^0 = \frac{\overline{R}}{p^0\mu_k^0}T; \tag{2.15}$$

$$v = \frac{\overline{R}}{p\mu_k}T. \tag{2.16}$$

Since $T = \text{const}$, and $v = v^0$ then, taking into consideration expressions (1.5) and (2.3) we obtain, that for a given fuel for the conditions indicated above the following relationship holds good:

$$p\mu = p^0\mu^0 = \text{const}. \tag{2.17}$$

The latter equation is remarkable. From a comparison of expressions (1.10), (1.15)–(1.17) and (2.2), (2.9)–(2.11), by taking into account (2.17) it follows immediately that the parameters X_O, X_C, X_H and X_N standing on the left-hand sides of the equations of material balance written for the dissociated combustion products (2.5)–(2.8), are equal to the corresponding parameters of equations (1.11)–(1.14) written for the combustion products without taking into account dissociation. Consequently

$$\left.\begin{aligned} X_O &= X_O^0; \\ X_C &= X_C^0; \\ X_H &= X_H^0; \\ X_N &= X_N^0. \end{aligned}\right\} \qquad (2.18)$$

The parameters X_O^0, X_C^0, X_H^0 and X_N^0 are easily determined according to formulae (1.10) and (1.15)–(1.17) for a given value of p^0 and a known elementary chemical composition of the fuel (A_O, A_C, A_H and A_N). The use of equation (2.17) also facilitates carrying out the calculation of the enthalpy of the combustion products under conditions of dissociation by formula (2.13).

Let us carry out together the obtaining of a system of equations, taking into account the fact that equation (2.14) has already been used:

$$\left.\begin{aligned}
&(1)\ \frac{p_{CO}\sqrt{p_{O_2}}}{p_{CO_2}} = K_1 = f_1(T); \\
&(2)\ \frac{p_{H_2}\sqrt{p_{O_2}}}{p_{H_2O}} = K_2 = f_2(T); \\
&(3)\ \frac{p_{OH}\sqrt{p_{H_2}}}{p_{H_2O}} = K_3 = f_3(T); \\
&(4)\ \frac{p_H}{\sqrt{p_{H_2}}} = K_4 = f_4(T); \\
&(5)\ \frac{p_O}{\sqrt{p_{O_2}}} = K_5 = f_5(T); \\
&(6)\ \frac{p_N}{\sqrt{p_{N_2}}} = K_6 = f_6(T); \\
&(7)\ \frac{p_{NO}}{\sqrt{p_{N_2}}\sqrt{p_{O_2}}} = K_7 = f_7(T); \\
&(8)\ X_O^0 = 2p_{CO_2} + 2p_{O_2} + p_{CO} + p_{H_2O} + p_O + p_{OH} + p_{NO}; \\
&(9)\ X_C^0 = p_{CO_2} + p_{CO}; \\
&(10)\ X_H^0 = 2p_{H_2O} + 2p_{H_2} + p_{OH} + p_H; \\
&(11)\ X_N^0 = 2p_{N_2} + p_{NO} + p_N; \\
&(12)\ i_T = i_{T_c}
\end{aligned}\right\} \qquad (2.19)$$

The composition of the mixture of gaseous combustion products in the presence of dissociation is, in the general case, a function of the following variables: A_O, A_C, A_H, A_N, p and T. This follows from the assumption that if the temperature, pressure and elementary chemical composition of a fuel be given, then the coefficients of the system of equations (2.19) are completely given, determining the sole solution of the problem. After making use of the supplementary relationships, the parameters A_C, A_H, α, p, T or X_C, X_H, α, p, T can also be used as independent variables. Obviously such a substitution is quite permissible.

5. Relationship between the Enthalpy of Dissociated Combustion Products and their Temperature

The chemical composition of the combustion products in the presence of dissociation is different from the composition of the combustion products determined without taking into account the dissociation reaction. The appearance additionally of such combustion products as OH, NO, H, N etc. changes (increases) the number of moles of combustion products per unit weight of the mixture. Together with the change in chemical composition of the combustion products, their thermodynamic parameters are also undoubtedly changed, in particular their enthalpy.

Following the method adopted by us for considering the parameters of the dissociated combustion products in two stages (see Section 4), we represent the enthalpy of 1 kg of dissociated combustion products i in the form of a sum:

$$i = i^0 + \Delta i. \qquad (2.20)$$

Here i^0 is the enthalpy of the undissociated combustion products.
Δi is the increment of the enthalpy of the mixture of combustion products as a result of dissociation.

Let us study the dependence of the parameter i on the temperature, for the combustion products of the fuels under consideration. Obviously, it will be determined by the dependence on temperature of the parameters i^0 and Δi.

Earlier, we obtained equations (1.36) and (1.37), thus enabling the enthalpy of the combustion products i^0 to be calculated in the absence of dissociation, at temperatures lying within the temperature regions H and L.

Let us consider the parameter Δi. Just like the other thermodynamic parameters, determined on the basis of the previously calculated chemical composition of the combustion products under dissociation conditions, the parameter Δi depends on the independent variables X_C, X_H, a, p, and T:

$$\Delta i = f(X_C,\ X_H,\ a,\ p \text{ and } T). \tag{2.21}$$

We shall exclude temporarily from the discussion the independent variable p, on the assumption that the change in Δi of temperature and of the other independent variables takes place at constant pressure of the combustion products. We shall denote the parameter Δi in this case by $\Delta i^{(p)}$.

It is obvious that under these conditions $\Delta i^{(p)}$ depends on the following independent variables:

$$\Delta i^{(p)} = f(X_C,\ X_H,\ a,\ T). \tag{2.22}$$

We shall study the function (2.22) with the object of obtaining simple, but sufficiently accurate analytical expressions connecting $\Delta i^{(p)}$ with the elementary chemical composition of the fuel and with the temperature of the combustion products. The limits of variation of the variables X_C, X_H and a we shall assume to be the same as for the case of the undissociated combustion products (see Table 3), and we shall divide the temperature region to be studied, as before, into the temperature region H and L. The pressure of the dissociated combustion products, for which the increase in enthalpy $\Delta i^{(p)}$ is determined, should be chosen beforehand.

The magnitude of the pressure of the dissociated combustion products should be sufficiently characteristic for the conditions of occurrence of the combustion products in rocket motors. In temperature region H (2800–3800°K), on the basis of the corresponding temperatures of the combustion products in the combustion chambers of engines, we shall carry out calculations of the parameter $\Delta i^{(p)}$ for a pressure $p_{H,\Phi} = 40$ atm. In temperature region L (1400–2800°K), on the basis of the corresponding temperatures of the combustion products in the discharge section of the engine nozzle, we shall carry out the calculations for a pressure of $p_{H,\Phi} = 1$ atm.

Let us investigate the nature of the dependence of the parameter $\Delta i^{(P)}$ on temperature in temperature region H (denoting it in this zone by $\Delta i_H^{(40)}$). We adopt the method of investigation similar to the method of processing results of physical measurement and consisting in the fact that the independent variable (in this case T) is assigned a number of values in the region of its variation and for each of them the value of the sought-for function is determined, after which the relationship is analysed. Only in our case the calculated values will assume the rôle of the measured values of the function. We shall carry out the investigation in the first place for the chemical compositions presented in Table 3 under the arbitrary numbers 1, 1_1, 4, 4_2, 4_3, 15, 15_1, and 15_2, since these compositions, as follows from consideration of their elementary chemical composition, are as if "limited" in relation to their content of the chemical elements nitrogen, hydrogen and carbon respectively. The calculations of the parameter $\Delta i_{\mathrm{H}}^{(40)}$, as also the other parameters related to the dissociated combustion products, will be made by the direct method, according to the known chemical composition of the combustion products, found as a result of solving the system of equations (2.19) for a pressure of the dissociated combustion products of 40 atm.

The results of the calculations are presented graphically in Fig. 2. The graph is constructed in logarithmic coordinates. Lines on the graph are drawn, as far as possible, close to the support points corresponding to the results of the calculations carried out (denoted on the graph by circles). Along the abscissa axis are laid off the values of log (T — 2200), and along the ordinate axis the values of $\log_{10}$ of the parameter $\Delta i_{\mathrm{H},v}^{(40)}$, related to $\Delta i_{\mathrm{H}}^{(40)}$ by the expression

$$\Delta i_{\mathrm{H},v}^{(40)} = 40\,\mu^0\,\Delta i_{\mathrm{H}}^{(40)}. \tag{2.23}$$

From consideration of the graph in Fig. 2 it follows that for specified chemical compositions, the relationship between $\Delta i_{\mathrm{H},v}^{(40)}$ and T is practically linear in logarithmic coordinates.

The linear relationship is maintained for values of the excess oxygen factor a from 0·60 to 0·90.

The angle of slope to the abscissa axis of the line relating to the composition with the simultaneous values X_{C} and X_{H}, but with different values of a, remains the same for all values of a taken for the calculation.

The magnitude of this angle is found to be in strict accordance with the initial elementary chemical composition (X_{C}, X_{H}) and increases with increase in carbon content. The minimum angle of flope of the line to the abscissa axis is recorded for cases of calculation os fuels with a high nitrogen content.

We shall carry out the study of the nature of the dependence of $\Delta i_{H,v}^{(40)}$ on the temperature for intermediate chemical compositions (denoted in Fig. 3 by the arbitrary numbers 2, 3, 5, 6, 8, 9, 10, 11, 12 and 14) only for values of the excess oxygen factor $a = 0{\cdot}90$,

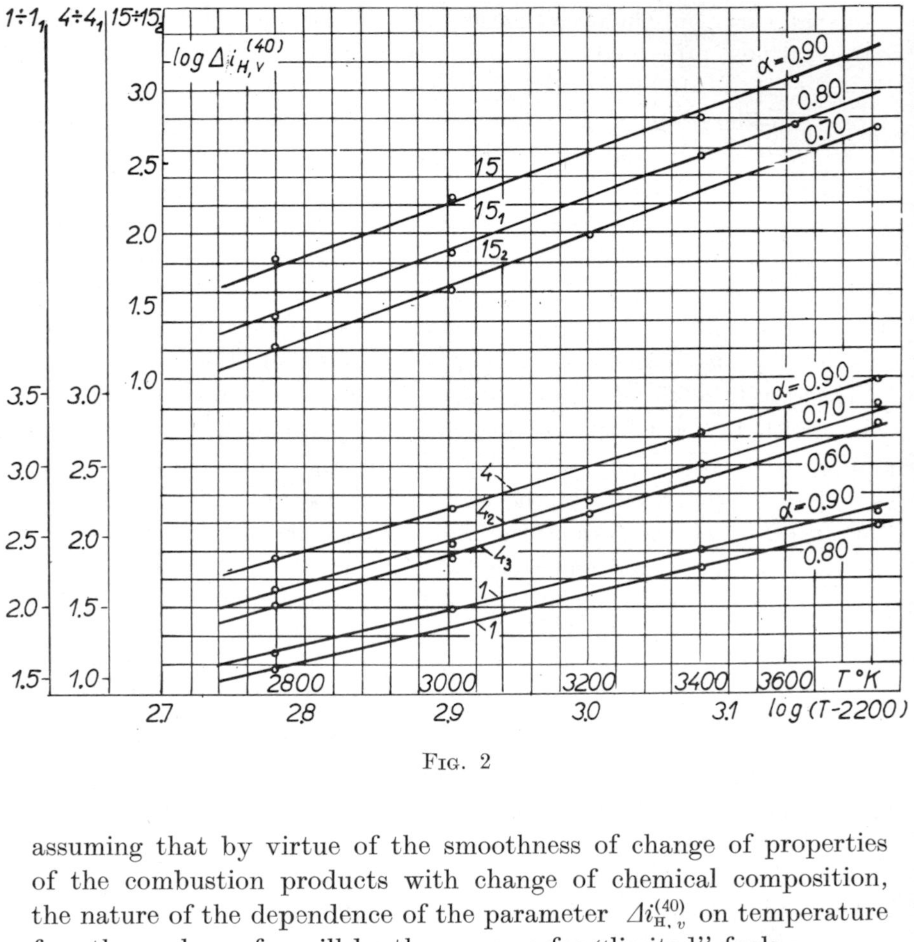

FIG. 2

assuming that by virtue of the smoothness of change of properties of the combustion products with change of chemical composition, the nature of the dependence of the parameter $\Delta i_{H,v}^{(40)}$ on temperature for other values of a will be the same as for "limited" fuels.

The results of the calculations for these compositions are presented graphically in Fig. 3. It follows from consideration of this graph that the establishment of the admissibility is also maintained for intermediate chemical compositions: the dependence of the parameter $\Delta i_{H,v}^{(40)}$ on temperature as a result of its graphical representation in logarithmic coordinates remains practically linear, and the angle formed by the straight line with the positive direction of the abscissa axis increases according to the extent of increase of the content of carbon in the fuel.

Consequently, it can be accepted with sufficient confidence that for all the compositions being considered, and within the entire

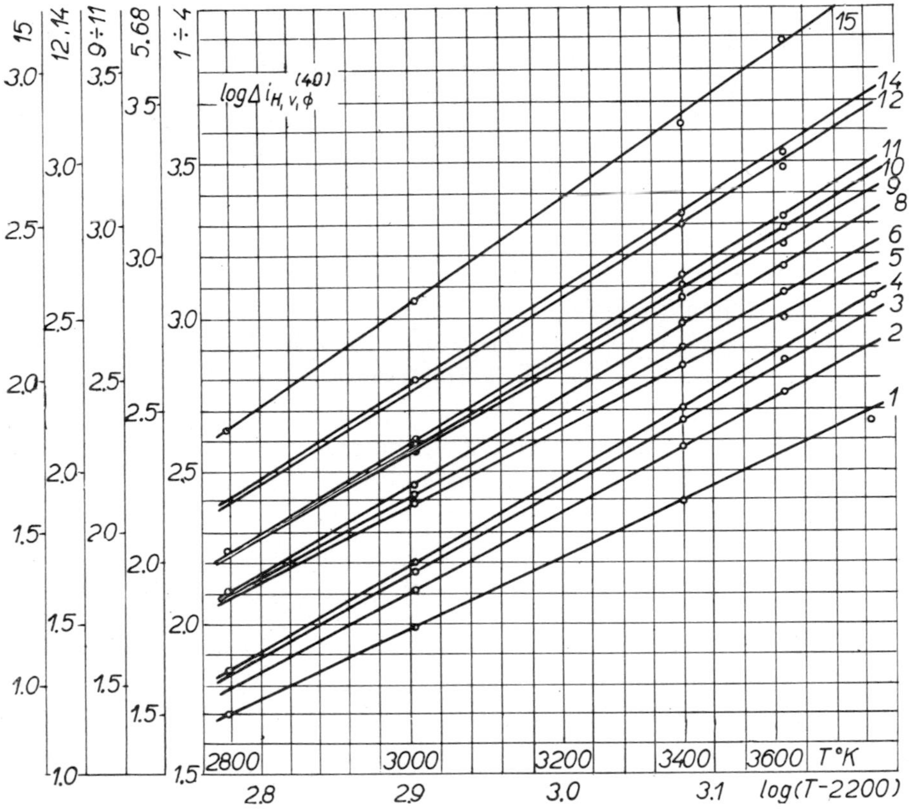

FIG. 3

temperature region H, there exists an approximate proportionality of the form

$$\log \Delta i^{(40)}_{H,\,v} \sim m_H \log (T - 2200)$$

or, transposing from the logarithmic form to the general form,

$$\Delta i^{(40)}_{H,\,v} \sim (T - 2200)^{m_H} . \qquad (2.24)$$

The power index m_H depends only on the parameters X_C and X_H, characterizing the initial chemical composition of the fuel, but is independent of the magnitude of a. The numerical value of the parameter m_H is equal to the tangent of the angle formed by the temperature axis and the straight lines representing the dependence of $\Delta i^{(40)}_{H,v}$ on temperature in the graphs, plotted in the coordinates mentioned above. The magnitude of the parameter m_H for the fuels considered in this work can be easily determined by the specially constructed nomogram presented in Fig. 7 of the Appendix. In order to construct the nomogram, the results of the same thermodynamic calculations are used which were carried out for establishing the form of the relationship between the parameter $\Delta i^{(40)}_{H,v}$ and the temperature. Along the abscissa on the nomogram are plotted the values of X_H. The lines of the graph correspond to fixed values of X_C. The sequence of the determination of the parameter m_H by the nomogram for known values of X_C and X_H requires no explanation.

We shall now investigate the dependence of the parameter Δi on the temperature T in temperature region L. We shall denote it by $\Delta i^{(1)}_L$. We shall employ here the same method of investigation which was adopted for temperature region H. We shall carry out direct calculations for determining the parameter $\Delta i^{(1)}_{L,v}$ (at the pressure of the dissociated combustion products $p_{L,\Phi} = 1$ atm) related to the parameter $\Delta i^{(1)}_L$ by the expression

$$\Delta i^{(1)}_{L,v} = \mu^0 \Delta i^{(1)}_L, \tag{2.25}$$

for different temperatures and for compositions denoted in Table 3 by the arbitrary numbers 1, 4, 4_1, 4_2, 4_3, 15, 15_1, 15_2, 15_3. The results of the calculations are presented graphically (Fig. 4).

The graph is constructed in logarithmic coordinates: along the abscissa axis are plotted the values of $\log (T - 1400)$, and along the ordinate axis the values of $\log \Delta i^{(1)}_{L,v}$. The support points through which the graph is drawn are denoted by circles. From consideration of the graph in Fig. 4 it follows that as a result of the graphical presentation of the relationship between the parameters $\Delta i^{(1)}_{L,v}$ and T in the coordinates [$\log \Delta i^{(1)}_{L,v}$; $\log (T - 1400)$], this relationship for the fuels being considered becomes practically linear. The linear relationship is maintained for values of the excess oxygen factor a from 0·60 to 0·90. The magnitude of the angle formed by the positive direction of the abscissa axis and the lines of the graph relating to the same composition (X_C, X_H) but different a, remains the same for all values of a taken for the calculation.

It is necessary to note that the linear relationship is observed to be worse at temperatures lying below 2200°K. The actual violation of the admissibility at relatively low temperatures may serve as a reason for this, as also the fact that the magnitude of the parameter $\Delta i^{(1)}_{L,v}$

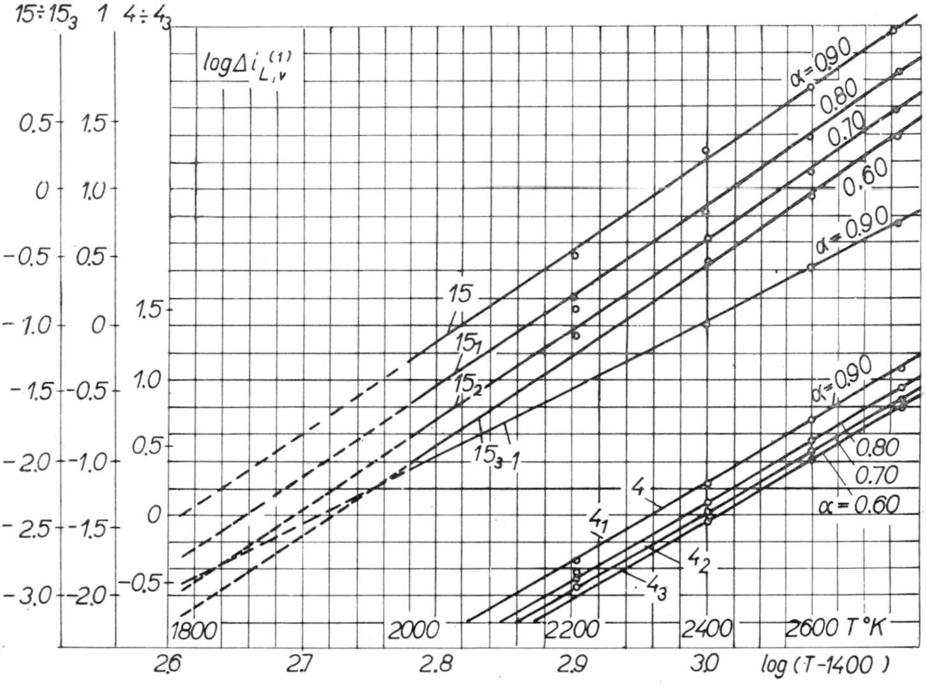

Fig. 4

becomes so small that marked errors might be allowed as a result of its calculation. However, in view of the absolute smallness of the magnitude of $\Delta i^{(1)}_{L,v}$ at these temperatures, it can be assumed that the establishment of a linear relationship is not violated also at temperatures below 2200°K.

Taking into consideration what has been said above, it can be accepted with sufficient reliability that for all compositions being considered and within the entire temperature region L, there is an approximate proportionality of the form

$$\log \Delta i^{(1)}_{L,v} \sim m_L \log (T - 1400),$$

or, transforming to the usual notation

$$\Delta i^{(1)}_{L,v} \sim (T - 1400)_{m_L}. \qquad (2.26)$$

The power index m_L depends only on the parameters X_C and X_H, characterizing the initial chemical composition of the fuel, but it is independent of the value of α. The numerical value of the parameter m_L for the fuels being considered can be determined by the nomogram presented in Fig. 8 of the Appendix. The nomogram is constructed similarly to the nomogram for determining the parameter m_H. No explanation is required for the sequence of operation with it.

Let us return to the temperature region H. Let us suppose that for the combustion products of any of the fuels being considered the value of the parameter $\Delta i_{H,v}^{(40)}$ is determined by direct calculation at a certain temperature $T_{H,\Phi}$ (and a pressure $p_{H,\Phi} = 40$ atm). We denote this by $\Delta i_{H,v,\Phi}$. In this case, in accordance with expression (2.24) the possibility emerges of calculating for a given fuel the value of the parameter $\Delta i_{H,v}^{(40)}$ at any temperature T (but for the same pressure $p_H = 40$ atm), without resorting to carrying out direct calculations for determining $\Delta i_{H,v}^{(40)}$ at this temperature. Actually, it follows from expression (2.24) that

$$\Delta i_{H,v}^{(40)} = \Delta i_{H,v,\Phi}\left(\frac{T - 2200}{T_{H,\Phi} - 2200}\right)^{m_H}. \tag{2.27}$$

The application of expression (2.27) to thermodynamic calculations of rocket engines is possible only in the case when a sufficiently simple method is found for determining the parameter $\Delta i_{H,v,\Phi}$ at a temperature $T_{H,\Phi}$ and a pressure $p_{H,\Phi} = 40$ atm for the combustion products of the fuels being considered.

There are possibilities for establishing such a method. The parameter $\Delta i_{H,v}$, determined for selected values of $T_{H,\Phi}$ and $p_{H,\Phi}$, is a function only of the initial chemical composition, i.e. of the independent variables X_C, X_H and α. It is advantageous to assign a series of values for the excess oxygen factor α and for each one of these to construct a nomogram for determining the parameter $\Delta i_{H,v,\Phi}$ for various values of X_C and X_H.

At what temperature $T_{H,\Phi}$ should the calculations of the parameter $\Delta i_{H,v,\Phi}$ be carried out and the nomograms be constructed? We mentioned earlier that the sought-for relationships in temperature region H will be used as the basis of calculation of the thermodynamic characteristics of the combustion products in the combustion chambers of rocket engines. According to these considerations, we choose $T_{H,\Phi} = 3400$°K.

In Figs. 9–14 of the Appendix are presented the nomograms for determining the parameter $\Delta i_{H,v,\Phi}$ for a pressure $p_{H,\Phi} = 40$ atm and a temperature $T_{H,\Phi} = 3400$ °K, constructed for values of α equal to 0·95; 0·90; 0·80; 0·70; 0·60; 0·55. The nomograms are constructed on the basis of direct calculation of the parameter $\Delta i_{H,v,\Phi}$ for the fuels shown in Table 3. Along the abscissa axis are plotted the values of the parameter X_H; the lines on the nomograms correspond to fixed values of the parameter X_C. The required quantity $\Delta i_{H,v,\Phi}$ is determined along the ordinate, at the point of intersection of the perpendicular erected to the abscissa axis from a point on the axis corresponding to the value of X_H, with the line corresponding to the value of X_C.

Taking into consideration expressions (2.23) and (2.27), we find the equation connecting the quantity $\Delta i_H^{(40)}$ in the temperature region H with the temperature of these products T (at a pressure $p_{H,\Phi} = 40$ atm):

$$\Delta i_H^{(40)} = \frac{\Delta i_{H,v,\Phi}}{40\,\mu^0}\left(\frac{T - 2200}{T_{H,\Phi} - 2200}\right)^{m_H}. \tag{2.28}$$

Joint consideration of equations (1.36), (2.20) and (2.28) enables a formula to be found for determining the enthalpy of 1 kg of dissociated combustion products in temperature region H (for a pressure of $p_{H,\Phi} = 40$ atm):

$$i_H^{(40)} = i_{2800}^0 + c_{p,H}^0 (T - 2800) + \frac{\Delta i_{H,v,\Phi}}{40\,\mu^0}\left(\frac{T - 2200}{T_{H,\Phi} - 2200}\right)^{m_H}. \tag{2.29}$$

Let us return to the temperature region L. We shall suppose that for the combustion products of any of the fuels being considered, the value is determined by direct calculation of the parameter $\Delta i_{L,v}^{(1)}$ for a certain temperature $T_{L,\Phi}$ (and for a pressure $p_{L,\Phi} = 1$ atm). We denote this by $\Delta i_{L,v,\Phi}$. In accordance with expression (2.26), in this case the possibility emerges of calculating for a given fuel the value of the parameter $\Delta i_{L,v}^{(1)}$ at any temperature T (but for the same pressure $p_{L,\Phi} = 1$ atm), without carrying out direct calculations for determining $\Delta i_{L,v}^{(1)}$ at these temperatures. Actually, it follows from (2.26) that

$$\Delta i_{L,v}^{(1)} = \Delta i_{L,v,\Phi}\left(\frac{T - 1400}{T_{L,\Phi} - 1400}\right)^{m_L}. \tag{2.30}$$

The parameter $\Delta i_{L,v,\Phi}$, determined for selected values of $p_{L\Phi}$ and $T_{L,\Phi}$, is a function of the independent variables X_C, X_H and α. It is convenient to assign a number of values for α, and for each one of them to construct a family of curves for determining the parameter $\Delta i_{L,v,\Phi}$ for different values of X_C and X_H.

The value of $T_{L,\Phi}$ should be close to the temperature of the combustion products in the discharge section of the nozzle. However, at the same time it should be sufficiently high so that dissociation of the combustion products should be appreciable and the numerical value of the parameter $\Delta i_{L,v\Phi}$ should be sufficiently large. Only in this case will the error in determining the parameter $\Delta i_{L,v,\Phi}$, as a result of its calculation, not exceed the permissible. We shall choose $T_{L,\Phi} = 2800$ °K according to these considerations.

In Figs. 15–20 of the Appendix are presented families of curves for determining the parameter $\Delta i_{L,v,\Phi}$ at a pressure of $p_{L,\Phi} = 1$ atm and a temperature $T_{L,\Phi} = 2800$ °K, constructed for the same values of a for which are constructed the families of curves for determining the parameter $\Delta i_{H,v,\Phi}$ in temperature region H.

The families of curves are constructed on the basis of direct calculations of the parameter $\Delta i_{L,v,\Phi}$ for the compositions presented in Table 3. The determination of the parameter $\Delta i_{L,v,\Phi}$ by the nomogram is carried out as for the determination of the parameter $\Delta i_{H,v,\Phi}$.

Taking into consideration expressions (2.25) and (2.30) we find

$$\Delta i_L^{(1)} = \frac{\Delta i_{L,v,\Phi}}{\mu^0}\left(\frac{T - 1400}{T_{L,\Phi} - 1400}\right)^{m_L}. \tag{2.31}$$

Solving concurrently expressions (1.37), (2.20) and (2.31) we obtain a formula for determining the enthalpy of 1 kg of dissociated combustion products in temperature region L (at a pressure of $p_{L,\Phi} = 1$ atm):

$$i_L^{(1)} = i_{2800}^0 + c_{p,L}^0 (T - 2800) + \frac{\Delta i_{L,v,\Phi}}{\mu^0}\left(\frac{T - 1400}{T_{L,\Phi} - 1400}\right)^{m_L}. \tag{2.32}$$

6. Relationship between the Increase in Enthalpy and the Increase in the Number of Moles of the Combustion Products as a Result of their Dissociation

Let us study the relationship

$$q = \frac{i - i^0}{M - M^0} = \frac{\Delta i}{\Delta M} \tag{2.33}$$

From consideration of expression (2.33) it can be concluded that the parameter q represents the ratio of the relating parameters inherent between them. As a result of dissociation of the combustion products of any of the fuels being considered, the number of moles of combustion products increases simultaneously as their enthalpy. The intensity of the increase of both parameters is determined primarily by the temperature of the combustion products and it is, to all appearances, approximately the same.

We shall investigate, for one of the types of fuel being considered, the effect on the value q of such independent variables as the elementary chemical composition of the fuel (X_C, X_H, a), the pressure p and the temperature T of the combustion products.

No precise analytical relationship exists between the quantities Δi and ΔM which would require no preliminary calculation of the composition of the combustion products. A study of the parameter q can be undertaken only by the results of direct calculation of the quantities Δi and ΔM for the combustion products of fuels of different chemical composition, at different temperatures and pressures. To this end, calculations have been carried out of the quantities Δi and ΔM, and thereby also for the parameter q, for the compositions marked in Table 3 by the arbitrary numbers from 1 to 15, for excess oxygen coefficients a from 0·60 to 0·99, for temperatures from 2400 to 3400 °K and for pressures of the dissociated combustion products from 1 to 40 atm.

The results of the calculations are presented in Table 5.

It follows from an analysis of the table, that for the compositions taken, at specified temperatures and pressures of the combustion products the parameter q is a practically constant quantity. The neutralized value of the parameter q, obtained from the results of 69 cases of calculation, is approximately 130:

$$q = \frac{\Delta i}{\Delta M} \cong 130. \tag{2.34}$$

The spread of values of the parameter q for different fuels does not exceed 8·5 per cent of its mean value, as can be seen from Table 5. This figure also includes, of course, the error which should be permitted for calculating q.

Table 5 embraces a somewhat broad class of chemical compositions, and also regions of temperature and pressure of the combustion products which it is difficult to surmise, and as a result of certain changes of conditions the relative constancy of q will not be maintained.

It is well-known that for a gradual change of chemical composition of the fuel, and also of the pressure and temperature of the combustion products, the thermodynamic parameters of the combustion products

TABLE 5

Arbitrary number of chemical composition	x_C	x_H	x_N	$p = 40$ atm, $T = 3400°$ K, a	$p = 40$ atm, $T = 3400°$ K, q	$p = 40$ atm, $T = 3000°$ K, a	$p = 40$ atm, $T = 3000°$ K, q	$p = 1$ atm, $T = 2800°$ K, a	$p = 1$ atm, $T = 2800°$ K, q	$p = 1$ atm, $T = 2400°$ K, a	$p = 1$ atm, $T = 2400°$ K, q
1	4	8	64	0·90	132·4	0·90	140·7	0·90	132·2	0·60	128·0
2	4	30	42	0·90	131·0	0·90	139·0	0·94	129·3	0·90	122·4
				0·76	129·0						
3	4	52	20	0·90	129·0	0·89	125·3	0·89	141·1	—	—
				0·62	128·7						
4	4	72	0	0·90	127·0	0·90	127·9	0·90	125·3	0·90	124·6
5	14	8	44	0·90	135·4	0·89	130·8	0·92	133·4	0·90	129·9
				0·63	122·6						
6	14	20	32	0·90	135·0	0·88	135·3	0·94	131·9	—	—
				0·66	128·7						
7	14	40	12	0·90	131·5	—	—	0·90	129·6	—	—
				0·71	127·4						
8	14	52	0	0·90	128·4	0·89	129·8	0·92	128·1	0·90	131·9
				0·70	124·7						
9	25	8	22	0·90	132·5	0·90	131·5	0·88	132·4	0·86	133·8
				0·66	127·6						
10	25	20	10	0·90	133·0	0·89	133·6	0·93	131·2	0·93	133·0
				0·67	128·6					0·87	134·6
11	25	30	0	0·90	132·0	0·90	130·7	0·92	129·5	0·93	131·7
				0·68	126·0					0·86	130·0
12	30	8	12	0·90	132·5	0·91	134·6	0·94	130·4	0·99	135·5
				0·68	131·2						
13	30	14	6	0·90	131·3	—	—	0·80	122·3	—	—
				0·70	130·0						
14	30	20	0	0·90	131·3	0·90	130·8	0·92	129·8	0·99	131·9
				0·70	127·1						
								0·90	130·0		
15	36	8	0	0·90	129·0	0·90	127·0	0·80	129·2	—	—
								0·70	127·3		

are changed uniformly, monotonically. The practice of carrying out thermodynamic calculations for rocket motors and the data from combustion experiments serves to confirm this.

7. Relationship between the Increase in Enthalpy of the Combustion Products as a Result of Dissociation and their Pressure

In the present section, the relationship will be investigated between the parameters Δi and p for the combustion products of the fuels being considered.

It is known that no analytical relationship exists between these parameters, which does not require a preliminary calculation of the composition of the combustion products. It has been established previously by other authors only that the relative increase of pressure of the combustion products, $\omega = \Delta p/p^0 = (p - p^0)/p^0$, under conditions of dissociation taking place at constant volume and temperature, depends on the absolute value of the pressure, so that the relationship is described by the approximate interpolating formula

$$\omega = B\, p^{-n_1}. \tag{2.35}$$

Here B is some coefficient and n_1 is a power index with respect to the absolute value, less than 1.

Formula (2.35) establishes that the increase in pressure of the combustion products as a result of dissociation is proportional to the fractional negative power of the pressure. In principle it gives the possibility of calculating the value of the parameter ω for any pressure p, if this value ω_x is known for a certain pressure p_x:

$$\omega = \omega_x \left(\frac{p}{p_x}\right)^{-n_1}. \tag{2.36}$$

A similar formula can also be written for the parameter Δi — the increase in enthalpy of the combustion products as a result of dissociation:

$$\Delta i = \Delta i_x \left(\frac{p}{p_x}\right)^{-n_2}. \tag{2.37}$$

It has been shown by a number of examples that the values of the power indices n_1 and n_2 are close to one another, so that for the combustion products of the fuels being considered in the case of $a < 1$, it can be assumed approximately that

$$n_1 = n_2 = 0{\cdot}5.$$

A satisfactory degree of accuracy in determining the parameters ω and Δi according to formulae (2.36) and (2.37) for the condition $n_1 = n_2 = 0{\cdot}5$ can be obtained only for close values of p and p_x. For values of p and p_x standing too remote from each other, the power index cannot be taken as equal to 0·5; it is necessary to determine it by a special calculation. In order to calculate the values of n_1 or n_2, the same formulae (2.36) or (2.37) can be used, having previously determined the parameters ω and Δi by direct calculation for not less than two values of pressure of the combustion products. In order to increase the accuracy of subsequent calculations, the parameter n_1 (or n_2) should be determined for values of pressure of the combustion products comparable with p and p_x respectively.

Besides the pressure, the temperature will also exert an influence on the quantities n_1 and n_2. In the general case the parameters n_1 and n_2 will depend on the chemical composition of the fuel, on the pressure and on the temperature. Thermodynamic calculations on rocket motors carried out by us show, however, that it is possible, without a large error in the final results of the calculations, to operate with a single value of the power index for a given fuel. We shall term this the effective power index n_{eff}.

The quantity n_{eff} should be determined for values of pressure and temperature of the combustion products characteristic of rocket motors. We shall assume, as before, that the characteristic pressure in the combustion chamber is a pressure of 40 atm, and in the exhaust section of the nozzle it is 1 atm. The temperature of the combustion products at which dissociation is observable is confined within the range being considered to the approximate values of 1800 and 3800 °K. The true dependence of n_1 (or n_2) on temperature is not known. It is known only that for an increase in the temperature of the combustion products, at which the calculation is carried out, the numerical value of the power index is evenly reduced in the majority of cases. Let us assume that between the parameters n_1 (or n_2) and the temperature within the limits 1800–3800°K there occurs a linear relationship. In this case, for the value of the parameter n_{eff} for temperatures of 1800–3800°K, the value of n_1 (or n_2) calculated for 2800°K can be adopted. Consequently,

$$n_{\text{eff}} \cong n_{2800} \tag{2.38}$$

The determination of n_{2800} for pressure values of 40 and 1 atm and a temperature of 2800 °K can be carried out via the parameter ω according to formula (2.36) or via Δi according to formula (2.37).

Using the inter-dependence of these quantities, as previously established, we shall prove that the values of n_1 and n_2 are close to each other.

Actually, since

$$\omega = \frac{\Delta p}{p} = \frac{\Delta M}{M^0},$$

then, in accordance with (2.34)

$$\frac{\Delta i}{\omega} = 130\, M^0 = \text{const}. \tag{2.39}$$

Hence, for a given fuel

$$n_1 = n_2 = \frac{\log w/w_x}{\log p_x/p} = \frac{\log \Delta i/\Delta i_x}{\log p_x/p} \tag{2.40}$$

Consequently, the equality of the values of n_1 and n_2 is observed to the same extent as the constancy of q for the fuels being considered.

In order to determine $n_{\text{eff}} = n_{2800}$ we find the increase in enthalpy of the combustion products at a temperature of 2800°K and a pressure of 40 atm by equation (2.28):

$$\Delta i_H^{(40)} = \frac{\Delta i_{H,\,v,\,\Phi}}{40\mu^0}\left(\frac{2800 - 2200}{T_{H,\,\Phi} - 2200}\right)^{m_H} = \frac{0{\cdot}5^{m_H}\,\Delta i_{H,\,v,\,\Phi}}{40\mu^0}$$

(since $T_{H,\,\Phi} = 3400$°K).

With this same objective we shall find, by formula (2.25), the value of $\Delta i_L^{(1)}$ for the same temperature of 2800°K (since $T_{L,\,\Phi} = 2800$°K) but for a pressure of 1 atm (or $p_{L,\,\Phi} = 1$ atm):

$$\Delta i_L^{(1)} = \frac{\Delta i_{L,\,v,\,\Phi}}{\mu^0}.$$

Then, in accordance with (2.37)

$$\frac{\Delta i_L^{(1)}}{\Delta i_H^{(40)}} = \frac{40\Delta i_{L,\,v,\,\Phi}}{0{\cdot}5^{m_H}\,\Delta i_{H,\,v,\,\Phi}} = \left(\frac{40}{1}\right)^{n_{\text{eff}}}$$

whence

$$n_{\text{eff}} = 0{\cdot}6242 \log \frac{40 \times 2^{m_H}\,\Delta i_{L,\,v,\,\Phi}}{\Delta i_{H,\,v,\,\Phi}}. \tag{2.41}$$

The parameters m_H, $\Delta i_{L,\,v,\,\Phi}$ and $\Delta i_{H,\,v,\,\Phi}$ are determined by calculation from a previously constructed nomogram.

With the determination of the parameter n_{eff}, the possibility emerges of calculating the increase in enthalpy as a result of dissociation of the combustion products for any pressure p, if the increase in enthalpy of these products is known for some chosen pressure (and for the same temperature). In temperature region H the curves in Figs.

9–14 of the Appendix make it possible to determine the increase in enthalpy $\Delta i_{H, v, \Phi}$ for a pressure of $p_{H, \Phi} = 40$ atm and a temperature $T_{H, \Phi} = 3400$ °K. For any other pressure in this region, but the same temperature of 3400°K, the increase in enthalpy will be equal to

$$\Delta i_{H, v}^{(3400)} = \Delta i_{H, v, \Phi} \left(\frac{p_{H, \Phi}}{p}\right)^{n_{\text{eff}}}. \tag{2.42}$$

By joint consideration of equations (2.28) and (2.42) we obtain an equation describing the dependence of the increase in enthalpy of 1 kg of combustion products Δi_H on the chemical composition of the fuel, the pressure and the temperature in temperature region H:

$$\Delta i_H = \frac{\Delta i_{H, v, \Phi}}{40\mu^0} \left(\frac{p_{H, \Phi}}{p}\right)^{n_{\text{eff}}} \left(\frac{T - 2200}{T_{H, \Phi} - 2200}\right)^{m_H}. \tag{2.43}$$

Denoting

$$c'_H = \frac{\Delta i_{H, v, \Phi}}{40\mu^0} \left(\frac{p_{H, \Phi}}{p}\right)^{n_{\text{eff}}}, \tag{2.44}$$

we obtain

$$\Delta i_H = c'_H \left(\frac{T - 2200}{T_{H, \Phi} - 2200}\right)^{m_H}. \tag{2.45}$$

The equation for the enthalpy of 1 kg of dissociated combustion products in temperature region H we shall determine as a result of the joint consideration of equations (1.36), (2.20) and (2.45):

$$i_H = i_{2800}^0 + c_{p,H}^0 (T - 2800) + c'_H \left(\frac{T - 2200}{T_{H, \Phi} - 2200}\right)^{m_H}. \tag{2.46}$$

In temperature region L, the curves in Figs. 15–20 of the Appendix make it possible to determine the increase in enthalpy $\Delta i_{L, v, \Phi}$ at a pressure of $p_{L, \Phi} = 1$ atm and a temperature $T_{L, \Phi} = 2800$°K. Consequently, for any other pressure in this zone, but for the same temperature, the increase in enthalpy of the combustion products is equal to

$$\Delta i_{L, v}^{(2800)} = \Delta i_{L, v, \Phi} \left(\frac{p_{L, \Phi}}{p}\right)^{n_{\text{eff}}}. \tag{2.47}$$

From the joint examination of equations (2.31) and (2.47) we obtain an equation describing the dependence of the increase in enthalpy of 1 kg of combustion products Δi_L on the chemical composition of the fuel, on the pressure and on the temperature in temperature region L.

$$\Delta i_L = \frac{\Delta i_{L, v, \Phi}}{\mu^0} \left(\frac{p_{L, \Phi}}{p}\right)^{n_{\text{eff}}} \left(\frac{T - 1400)}{T_{L, \Phi} - 1400}\right)^{m_L}. \tag{2.48}$$

Denoting

$$c'_L = \frac{i_{L, \Phi}}{\mu^0} \left(\frac{p_{L, \Phi}}{p}\right)^{n_{\text{eff}}}, \tag{2.49}$$

we obtain

$$\Delta i_L = c'_L \left(\frac{T - 1400}{T_{L,\Phi} - 1400}\right)^{m_L}. \tag{2.50}$$

The equation for the enthalpy of 1 kg of dissociated combustion products in temperature region L we shall determine from joint examination of equations (1.37), (2.20) and (2.50):

$$i_L = i^0_{2800} = c^0_{p,L}(T - 2800) + c'_L \left(\frac{T - 1400}{T_{L,\Phi} - 1400}\right)^{m_L}. \tag{2.51}$$

8. Entropy of the Combustion Products

The aim of this section is to find equations which will enable the value to be calculated of the entropy of the dissociated combustion products at a temperature T and pressure p, without preliminary calculation of their chemical composition.

We shall choose as parameters for the initial reading of the entropy the temperature $T_1 = 1400$°K and the pressure $p_1 = 1$ atm. The temperature $T_1 = 1400$°K is the lower limit of the region of temperature being considered and therefore its choice as the initial temperature does not require additional explanation. It should be mentioned that the choice of any other temperature for the initial reading of the entropy would have no influence on the results of thermodynamic calculations on engines, since the absolute value of the entropy exerts no influence on these results. We shall assume that for these initial conditions the entropy of the combustion products, consisting of carbon dioxide gas, carbon monoxide, water vapour and diatomic nitrogen and hydrogen existing amongst themselves in a state of chemical equilibrium, is equal to S_0.

The conversion from the initial parameters of the combustion products T_1 and p_1 to a given T and p can be developed by means of the following three reversible processes, the change of entropy for which is determined quite simply. The determination of the entropy in all these processes is carried out by integrating the following differential equation:

$$\mathrm{d}S = \frac{\mathrm{d}i}{T} - v\frac{\mathrm{d}p}{T}. \tag{2.52}$$

First Process. The combustion products are reversibly compressed from a pressure $p_1 = 1$ atm to a high pressure p^0 at constant temperature $T_1 = 1400$°K. During this process the chemical composition of the combustion products is unchanged, and therefore the change in enthalpy of the combustion products $di = 0$ (the combustion products are, by definition, an ideal gas).

The change in entropy in this process is found by integrating expression (2.52) for $T = \text{const}$ and $\mu^0 = \text{const}$.

It is equal to $\Delta S_1 = -\frac{\bar{R}}{\mu_0} \ln p^0$. (2.53)

Second Process. The combustion products are reversibly heated at constant pressure p^0 (without dissociation) from a temperature $T_1 = 1400°K$ to a temperature T. The enthalpy of the combustion products up to a temperature of 2800°K is determined in this case by expression (2.51), and above 2800°K by expression (2.46). Substituting these values in expression (2.52) and integrating it for constant pressure $p^0 = \text{const}$, we find the change in entropy in the second process, in the case when the value of the temperature T is found within temperature region H (2800–3800°K):

$$\Delta S_{2,\,H} = \int_{1400}^{2800} \frac{di_L^0}{T} + \int_{2800}^{T} \frac{di_H^0}{T} =$$

$$= c^0_{p,\,L} \ln \frac{2800}{1400} + c^0_{p,\,H} \ln \frac{T}{2800}. \tag{2.54}$$

If the value of the temperature T is found within temperature region L (1400–2800°K), then

$$\Delta S_{2,L} = \int_{1400}^{T} \frac{di_L^0}{T} = c^0_{p,\,L} \ln \frac{T}{2800}. \tag{2.55}$$

Third Process. The combustion products are expanded reversibly from a pressure p° to the value p of the pressure being considered, at constant value of the final temperature T. The change in entropy in the third process is equal to:

$$\Delta S_3 = \frac{1}{T} \int_{p^0}^{p} (di - v\,dp) = \frac{i - i^0}{T} - \int_{p^0}^{p} \frac{\bar{R}\,(1+\omega)}{\mu^0 p}\,dp =$$

$$= \frac{\Delta i}{T} - \frac{\bar{R}}{\mu_0} \ln \frac{p}{p^0} - \frac{\bar{R}}{\mu^0} \int_{p_0}^{p} \frac{\omega\,dp}{p}, \tag{2.56}$$

since

$$\mu = \frac{\mu^0}{1+\omega}. \tag{2.57}$$

The relative fraction of the last term of expression (2.56) amounts to 4–8 per cent of the overall change of entropy. Therefore, the integral $\int_{p^0}^{p} \frac{\omega\, dp}{p}$ can be evaluated to a great degree of accuracy. From expression (2.39) we obtain

$$\omega = \frac{\mu^0 \Delta i}{130}.$$

Consequently,

$$\int_{p^0}^{p} \frac{\omega dp}{p} = \frac{\mu^0}{130} \int_{p^0}^{p} \frac{\Delta i dp}{p}.$$

Substituting the value of $\Delta\, i_H$, given by expression (2.43), we find the value of this integral for the case of temperature region H:

$$\left(\int_{p^0}^{p} \frac{\omega\, dp}{p}\right)_H = \frac{\Delta i_{H,\,v,\,\Phi}}{40 \cdot 130} \left(\frac{T - 2200}{T_{H,\Phi} - 2200}\right)^{m_H} p_{H,\,\Phi}^{n_{\text{eff}}} \int_{p^\circ}^{p} \frac{dp}{p^{n_{\text{eff}}+1}},$$

since the parameters $\Delta\, i_{H,\,v,\,\Phi}$, n_{eff}, $T_{H,\,\Phi}$, $p_{H,\Phi}$ and m_H are independent of the pressure.

Since a dissociation reaction is absent at pressure p^0, then

$$\int_{p^0}^{p} \frac{dp}{p^{n_{\text{eff}}+1}} = -\frac{1}{n_{\text{eff}}\, p^{n_{\text{eff}}}}.$$

Consequently, for the case of temperature region H

$$\left(\int_{p^0}^{p} \frac{\omega dp}{p}\right)_H = -\frac{c'_H \mu^0}{130\, n_{\text{eff}}} \left(\frac{T - 2200}{T_{H,\Phi} - 2200}\right)^{m_H}, \tag{2.58}$$

where c_H is determined by expression (2.44).

Similarly, we find the value of the integral for the case of temperature region L:

$$\left(\int_{p^0}^{p} \frac{\omega\, dp}{p}\right)_L = +\frac{c'_L\, \mu^0}{130\, n_{\text{eff}}} \left(\frac{T - 1400}{T_{L,\Phi} - 1400}\right)^{m_L}, \tag{2.59}$$

where c'_L is determined by expression (2.49).

The entropy of the combustion products having a temperature T and pressure p is equal to

$$S = S_0 + \Delta\, S_1 + \Delta\, S_2 + \Delta\, S_3.$$

For the calculations there is no necessity to know the absolute value of the entropy of the combustion products, but only the difference in entropy occurring in the processes under consideration need be known. Therefore, the value of the initial entropy S_0 can be taken as arbitrary. For the sake of simplicity of the calculated formula, we choose the initial value of the entropy equal to

$$S_0 = -c^0_{p,\,L} \ln \frac{2800}{1400}. \tag{2.60}$$

The equation for the entropy of the combustion products for the case of temperature region H is determined from joint examination of expressions (2.53), (2.54), (2.56), (2.58), (2.60):

$$S_H = 2{\cdot}303\, c^0_{p,\,H} \log \frac{T}{2800} - 2{\cdot}303\, \frac{\overline{R}}{\mu^0} \log p + \\ + c'_H \left(\frac{T - 2200}{T_{H,\,\Phi} - 2200}\right)^{m_H} \left(\frac{1}{T} + \frac{\overline{R}}{130 n_{\text{eff}}}\right). \tag{2.61}$$

Similarly, for the case of temperature region L we obtain

$$S_L = 2{\cdot}303\, c^0_{p,\,L} \log \frac{T}{2800} - 2{\cdot}303\, \frac{\overline{R}}{\mu^0} \log p + \\ + c'_L \left(\frac{T - 1400}{T_{L,\,\Phi} - 1400}\right)^{m_L} \left(\frac{1}{T} + \frac{\overline{R}}{130 n_{\text{eff}}}\right). \tag{2.62}$$

Equations (2.61) and (2.62) enable the entropy of the combustion products to be calculated at their pressure p and temperature T without preliminary calculation of their chemical composition. These equations, used together with the equations previously established for the enthalpy of the combustion products and with the nomograms presented in this book, enable a new method to be developed for the thermodynamic assessment of rocket motors operating on the fuels under consideration. The methods of assessment of engines by the new method are discussed in the next chapter.

CHAPTER 3

Method of Thermodynamic Assessment of Liquid Rocket Engines

9. Temperature of the Combustion Products in the Combustion Chamber of an Engine

Let us suppose that we are given the components of a fuel — combustible and oxidant, and that their chemical composition, the value of the excess oxidant coefficient α_0' at which they burn in the combustion chamber of the engine, and also the pressure of the combustion products $P_{c\cdot c}$ are known. It is required to find the temperature of the combustion products of the fuel under the stated conditions.

By carrying out the calculation for those premises and assumptions which are enumerated in the "Introduction", the theoretical temperature of the combustion products in the combustion chamber of an engine $T_{c\cdot c}$ is determined from the conditions of equilibrium of the enthalpy of unit weight (1 kg) of combustion products with the enthalpy of the same unit weight of fuel:

$$i_f = i_{T_{c\cdot c}}. \tag{3.1}$$

The enthalpy of unit weight (1 kg) of fuel may be known or may be found by separate calculation. The method of determining it is shown in Section 20 of this book. Here we shall assume that the value of the parameter i is known.

In order to calculate the value of the temperature $T_{c\cdot c}$ we shall use the following order of calculation.

1. The content by weight of the chemical elements in 1 kg of oxidant is determined in grams:

$$C_o,\ H_o,\ N_o,\ O_o.$$

2. The content by weight of the chemical elements in 1 kg of combustible is determined in grams:

$$C_c,\ H_c,\ N_c,\ O_c.$$

3. The quantity of oxidant necessary for the oxidation of 1 kg of combustible is determined

$$\nu_o = \frac{8/3\,C_c + 8H_c - O_c}{O_o - 8/3\,C_o - 8H_o}\,. \qquad (3.2)$$

4. Certain values are assigned for the excess oxidant coefficient a, viz, those for which the curves in Figs. 1–6 and Figs. 9–20 in the Appendix are constructed (0·95; 0·90; 0·80; 0·70; 0·60; 0·55.), and the values of the excess oxidant coefficient corresponding to them are determined by the formula

$$a_o = \frac{1}{\nu_0}\,\frac{8/3\,C_c + 8H_c - O_c/a}{\dfrac{O_o}{a} - \dfrac{8}{3}C_o - 8H_o}\,. \qquad (3.3)$$

The value of a' corresponding to a given a_0' is determined:

$$a' = \frac{O_c + a_0'\nu_o}{\dfrac{8}{3}(C_c + a_0'\nu_o C_o) + 8(H_c + a_0' H_o)}\,. \qquad (3.3a)$$

5. The weight ratio of the fuel components ν is calculated for selected values of a and the derived value of a', according to the formul,

$$\nu = a_0\,\nu_0. \qquad (3.4)$$

6. The number of g-atoms is found of the chemical elements carbona hydrogen and nitrogen in 1 kg of fuel for selected values of a and the derived value a', according to the formulae

$$\left.\begin{aligned} A_C &= \frac{C_c + \nu C_o}{12(1+\nu)}\,; \\ A_H &= \frac{H_c + \nu H_o}{1+\nu}\,; \\ A_N &= \frac{N_c + \nu N_o}{14(1+\nu)}\,. \end{aligned}\right\} \qquad (3.5)$$

7. For the selected values of a and with the derived value of a', the parameter μ^0 is determined by the formula

$$\mu^0 = \frac{1}{M^0} = \frac{1}{A_C + 0{\cdot}5(A_H + A_N)}\,. \qquad (3.6)$$

Formula (3.6) is obtained from joint examination of expressions (1.4), (1.5) and (1.7).

8. The values of the parameters $X_C = X_C^0$ and $X_H = X_H^0$ are found from formulae (1.39) and (1.40), for selected values of a and for the derived value of a':

$$X_C = 40\ \mu^0\ A_C; \tag{1.39}$$

$$X_H = 40\ \mu^0\ A_H. \tag{1.40}$$

9. The value of the parameters i_v^0, $\Delta i_{H,v,\Phi}$ and $\Delta i_{L,v,\Phi}$ are determined by the curves in Figs. 1–6 and 9–20 of the Appendix for selected values of a.

10. A supplementary graph is constructed, showing the change of the parameters i_v^0, $\Delta i_{H,v,\Phi}$ and $\Delta i_{L,v,\Phi}$ as a function of change of a.

11. The values of the parameters i_v^0, $\Delta i_{H,v,\Phi}$ and $\Delta i_{L,v,\Phi}$ corresponding to the given value of the excess oxidant coefficient a_0' (i.e. the derived value of a') are determined by graphical interpolation methods.

In future we shall carry out the calculation of the temperature of the combustion products in the combustion chamber of the engine, $T_{c\cdot c}$, in accordance with the conditions of the problem, only for the derived value of a'. The value of $T_{c\cdot c}$ usually lies within temperature region H, i.e. above 2800°K. Its determination is mostly undertaken by equation (2.46). We shall show the method of calculation of the temperature $T_{c\cdot c}$ by this equation.

12. From the curves in Fig. 7 of the Appendix, the value is found of the parameter m_H.

13. The value is calculated of the parameter $c_{p,H}$ by formula (1.42).

14. The value is calculated of the parameter n_{eff} by formula (2.41).

15. The value is calculated of the parameter i_{2800}^0 by formula (1.41).

16. The value is calculated of the parameter c_H' by formula (2.44), assuming $p = p_{c\,c}$. For this $p_{H,\Phi} = 40$ atm.

17. Equation (2.46) is written down as applicable to our case

$$i_f = i_{2800}^0 + c_{p,H}^0 (T_{c,c} - 2800) + c_H' \left(\frac{T_{c,c} - 2200}{T_{H,\Phi} - 2200}\right)^{m_H}.$$

We assign to this equation a form convenient for calculating $T_{c\cdot c}$: terms independent of temperature we transfer to the left-hand side of the equation and the algebraic sum of the terms of the left-hand side we denote by i_k:

$$i_k = i_f - i_{2800}^0 + 2800\, c_{p,H}^0. \tag{3.7}$$

Then, taking into consideration that $T_{H,\Phi} = 3400°\text{K}$, we obtain

$$i_k = c^0_{p,H} T_{c\cdot c} + c'_H \left(\frac{T_{c,c} - 2200}{1200}\right)^{m_H}. \tag{3.8}$$

It is recommended that the value of the temperature $T_{c\cdot c}$ be determined from the equation in the following manner: assign 3–4 values of the temperature T_{ki}, close to the anticipated temperature of the combustion products in the combustion chamber $T_{c\cdot c}$, and by equation (3.8) find the values corresponding to it of the enthalpy i_{ki}. Then, from the condition $i_{k,i} = i_k$ the unknown value of $T_{c.c}$ is found by one or other method.

In those cases when the anticipated value of the temperature $T_{c\cdot c}$ is found below 2800°K (in temperature region L) equation (2.51) is used for its determination.

10. Entropy of the Combustion Products in the Combustion Chamber of an Engine

The value of the entropy of the combustion products in the combustion chamber of an engine for temperatures of the combustion products of 2800°K and above is found by equation (2.61). For the given case the equation assumes the form:

$$S_{c\cdot c} = 2{\cdot}303 c^0_{p,H} \log \frac{T_{c.c}}{2800} - \frac{0{\cdot}004574}{\mu^0} \log p_{c\cdot c} +$$

$$+ c'_H \left(\frac{T_{c.c} - 2200}{1200}\right)^{m_H} \left(\frac{1}{T_{c.c}} + \frac{1{\cdot}527 \times 10^{-5}}{n_{\text{eff}}}\right). \tag{3.9}$$

Here it is assumed that $S_{c\,c} = S_H$, $T = T_{c\cdot c}$, $p = p_{c\cdot c}$, $\bar{R} = 0{\cdot}001986$ kcal/deg.

The values of the parameters $c^0_{p,H}$, μ^0, c'_H, m_H and n_{eff} were determined earlier.

For temperatures of the combustion products in the combustion chamber of the engine, not attaining 2800 °K, calculation of their entropy is carried out by equation (2.62).

11. Temperature and Enthalpy of the Combustion Products in the Exhaust Section of the Engine Nozzle

The temperature of the combustion products in the exhaust section of the nozzle is determined as arising from the premises assumed in this book, in accordance with which the expansion of the combustion products and their discharge from the engine takes place reversibly without loss and supply of energy.

In this case the entropy of the combustion products $S_{c \cdot c}$ is equal to their entropy in the exhaust section of the nozzle S_{exh}.

$$S_{c \cdot c} = S_{exh} \tag{3.10}$$

We shall assume for this that the value of the entropy $S_{c.c}$ found by us according to the method described in the previous section, and the pressure of the combustion products in the exhaust section of the nozzle, p_{exh}, is given.

The temperature of the combustion products in the exhaust section of the nozzle T_{exh}, lies, in the absolute majority of cases, within the temperature region L, i.e. below 2800°K. In order to find it, equation (2.62) must usually be used. First of all we determine the value of certain of the parameters entering into equation (2.62).

1. We calculate the value of the parameter $c^0_{p,L}$ according to formula (1.43).

2. The value of the parameter m_L is determined from the curves of Fig. 8 in the Appendix.

3. We calculate the value of the parameter c'_L by formula (2.49), assuming $p = p_{exh}$. For this, $p_{L,\Phi} = 1$ atm.

We write down equation (2.62) in a form convenient for calculating the value of T_{exh}. With this in mind, we transpose all the terms of the equation which are independent of the temperature to the left-hand side, and we denote the algebraic sum of the terms of the left-hand side, by S_a. Assuming $\overline{R} = 0{\cdot}001986$ kcal/deg, we obtain

$$S_a = S_{c \cdot c} + 2{\cdot}303 c^0_{p,L} \log 2800 + \frac{0{\cdot}004574}{\mu^0} \log p_{exh}. \tag{3.11}$$

In this case

$$S_a = 2{\cdot}303 c^0_{p,L} \log T_a + c'_L \left(\frac{T_{exh} - 1400}{1400}\right)^{m_L} \left(\frac{1}{T_{exh}} + \frac{1{\cdot}527 \times 10^{-5}}{n_{eff}}\right) \tag{3.12}$$

(since $T_{L,\Phi} = 2800$°K).

The value of the temperature T_{exh} according to equation (3.12) is best determined in the following manner: certain values of the temperature $T_{exh,i}$ are assigned, close to the expected value of T_{exh}, and for each of them the value of the entropy S_{ai} is found according to equation (3.12). Further from the condition $S_{ai} = S_a$ we determine the true value of the temperature T_{exh}.

For $S_a/c^0_{p,L} \leqslant 7{\cdot}50$ the evaluation of T_{exh} can be carried out according to the formula

$$\log T_{exh} = \frac{S_a}{2{\cdot}303 c^0_{p,L}}. \tag{3.13}$$

In this case $T_{exh} \leqslant 1800°K$.

The value of the enthalpy of the combustion products in the exhaust section of the nozzle i_{exh} is found by equation (2.51). In order to solve the equation it is necessary to assume $i_L = i_{exh}$, $T = T_{exh}$, $p = p_{exh}$, $T_{L\Phi} = 2800°K$, and $p_{L\Phi} = 1$ atm.

12. Exhaust Velocity of the Combustion Products and the Specific Thrust for a calculated Operating Régime of the Engine

The ideal exhaust velocity of the combustion products is determined according to the equation

$$w_{exh} = 91{\cdot}53 \sqrt{(i_f - i_{exh})}. \tag{3.14}$$

The specific thrust for a calculated operating régime of the engine is determined according to the equation

$$P_{sp} = \frac{w_{exh}}{g} \frac{\text{kg}}{\text{kg/sec}}. \tag{3.15}$$

13. Specific Volume of the Combustion Products

In those circumstances when the thrust of the engine is given, a thermodynamic calculation can be carried out with the object of determining the basic dimensions of the combustion chamber. For this it is necessary to determine the specific volumes of the combustion products in different sections of the chamber.

We shall show the method of calculation of the specific volume of the combustion products by using the approximate mathematical expressions established in this book. In accordance with (2.34) the number of moles of dissociated combustion products in 1 kg of them is equal to

$$M = M^0 + \Delta i/130.$$

Here Δi is expressed in kcal/kg.

It is also known that

$$M = \frac{1000}{\mu_k} = \frac{1000}{848} R,$$

where R is the gas constant for the dissociated combustion products in kg/kg/deg, Consequently,

$$R = 0{\cdot}848\, M^{0} + 0{\cdot}00652\, \Delta i. \tag{3.16}$$

For the case of the combustion chamber of an engine, the gas constant of the combustion products will be equal to

$$R_{c\cdot c} = 0{\cdot}848\, M^{0} + 0{\cdot}00652\, \Delta i_{c\cdot c}$$

where

$$i_{c\cdot c} = c'_{H} \left(\frac{T_{exh} - 2200}{1200} \right)^{m_H}.$$

For the conditions of the exhaust section of the nozzle, the gas constant is equal to

$$R_{exh} = 0{\cdot}848\, M^{0} + 0{\cdot}00652\, \Delta i_{exh},$$

where

$$\Delta i_{exh} = c'_{L} \left(\frac{T_{exh} - 1400}{1400} \right)^{m_L}.$$

The specific volumes of the combustion products in the combustion chamber of the engine and in the exhaust section of the nozzle are determined by the equations

$$v_{c.c} = \frac{R_{c.c}\, T_{c.c}}{p_{c.c}}; \tag{3.17}$$

$$v_{exh} = \frac{R_{exh}\, T_{exh}}{P_{exh}}. \tag{3.18}$$

The index of the adiabatic flow is defined by the well known expression

$$k = \frac{\log \left(\frac{p_{c.c}}{p_{exh}} \right)}{\log \left(\frac{p_{c.c}}{p_{exh}} \frac{T_{exh}}{T_{c.c}} \right)}. \tag{3.19}$$

Thus, the method of calculation adopted makes it possible to establish the basic dimensions of the combustion chamber of an engine, without resorting to calculation of the chemical composition of the combustion products.

14. Methods of carrying out Thermodynamic Calculations in certain Special Case

(A) *Effect of Excess Oxidant Coefficient of the fuel on the Operating Characteristics of the Engine*

In carrying out thermodynamic calculations of rocket motors it is frequently required to establish the relationship between the magnitudes of the most important operating parameters of an engine: the temperatures of the combustion products in the combustion chamber and in the exhaust section of the nozzle, the exhaust velocity, specific thrust etc, and the excess oxidant coefficient a_0.

We shall set forth the most acceptable order for carrying out thermodynamical calculations in this case. We shall assume that the chemical composition of the combustible and of the oxidant is given and also that the pressure of the combustion products in the combustion chamber $p_{c \cdot c}$ and in the exhaust section of the nozzle p_{exh} are given. It is required to carry out the investigation for values of the excess oxidant coefficient a_0 within the arbitrary limits of 0·95 to 0·55.

In order to solve the set problem, we shall assign a series of values for the excess oxidant coefficient a from these limits, for which nomograms are constructed, and for each one of them we shall successively determine the values of the parameters a_0, ν, A_C, A_H, A_N, μ_0, X^c, X_H, and by the curves in Figs. 1–20 of the Appendix we shall determine the values of the parameters i_v^0, m_H, m_L, $\Delta i_{H, v, \Phi}$ $\Delta i_{L, v, \Phi}$. Further, for each value assigned for a we shall carry through the calculations to completion by successively determining the values of the parameters i_f, $c^0_{p\,H}$, i^0_{2800}, n_{eff}, c'_H, $T_{c \cdot c}$, and also $S_{c \cdot c}$, S_a, $c^0_{p,L}$, C'_L, T_{exh}, i_{exh}, W_{exh}, and P_{sp}.

Having determined the values of the unknown parameters for all chosen values of a, we shall construct a graph of the dependence of these parameters on the excess oxidant coefficient and from it we shall find the values of the parameters for any intermediate values of a_0.

(B) *Effect of Pressure of the Combustion Products in the Combustion Chamber of the Engine on the Operating Characteristics of the Engine*

We shall assume that it is required to establish the effect of change of the combustion products in the combustion chamber of an engine on the operating characteristics of the engine. For this, bearing in mind the approximate nature of the mathematical expression established earlier, we shall confine the study of the range of variation of pressure of the combustion products in the combustion chamber to the limits of 20 to 100 atm. The least error in the values of the unknown parameters is obtained in the case of calculation for a pressure of the combustion products in the combustion chamber of 40 atm (the curves in Figs. 9–14 of the Appendix are constructed for a pressure of 40 atm). At higher pressures the effect of dissociation is reduced and the use of the approximate expressions established earlier also does not lead to significant errors in the values of the unknown parameters. For pressures of the combustion products in the combustion chamber of an engine of less than 40 atm, the degree of accuracy of the calculation is reduced, since it is greater the lower is the pressure. At these pressures dissociation reactions are extremely well-developed and the approximate nature of the expressions obtained begins to be exerted on the results of the calculations.

We shall assume that the chemical composition of the combustible and of the oxidant, the value α_0', and this means also the value of α' (for simplicity we shall assume that α' conforms with one of the values of α for which the curves in Figs. 1–6 and 9–20 of the Appendix are constructed), and the magnitude of the pressure of the combustion products in the exhaust section of the nozzle p_{exh} are known. The special feature of carrying out the calculations in the given case consists in the fact that the values of all the parameters which are independent of the pressure of the combustion products, can be determined beforehand and then used for any values whatsoever of p_{exh}.

Consequently, we shall determine in the first place, for a given α' the values of the parameters v, A_{C}, A_{H}, A_{N}, μ^0, X_{C}, X_{H} and by means of the curves in Figs. 1–20 of the Appendix the values of the parameters i_v^0, m_H, m_L, $\Delta i_{H,v,\Phi}$, $\Delta i_{L,v,\Phi}$.

Further, we shall assign a series of values for the pressure of the combustion products in the combustion chamber of the engine $p_{\text{c·c}}$ and for each one of them we shall carry through the calculation, determining in succession the parameters

$$c_{\text{H}}',\ S_{\text{c·c}},\ S_a,\ c_L',\ T_{\text{exh}},\ w_{\text{exh}},\ \text{and}\ P_{\text{sp}}.$$

Having determined the values of the unknown parameters for all chosen values of $p_{\text{c·c}}$, we shall construct a graph of the dependence of these parameters on the pressure of the combustion products in the combustion chamber and from it we shall find the values of the parameters for any intermediate values of $p_{\text{c·c}}$.

(C) *Effect of Pressure of the Combustion Products in the Exhaust Section of the Nozzle on the Operating Characteristics of an Engine*

We shall suppose that it is required to establish the effect of change of pressure of the combustion products in the exhaust section of the nozzle on the above-mentioned operating characteristics of an engine. For this we shall assume that the chemical composition of the combustible and of the oxidant and the pressure of the combustion products in the combustion chamber of the engine $p_{c\cdot c}$ are known.

The special feature of carrying out the calculations in the given case is the invariability of the characteristics of the combustion products (in the first place the temperature $T_{c\cdot c}$) for all values of pressure of the combustion products in the exhaust section of the nozzle.

We shall carry out the following succession of calculations.

1. For specified values of α_0' (α') and $p_{c\cdot c}$ we shall carry out the calculation of the parameters whose values are independent of the magnitude of p_{exh}:

$$\nu, A_C, A_H, A_N, \mu^0, X_C X_H, i_v^0, m_H, m_L,$$

$$\Delta i_{H, v, \Phi}, \Delta i_{L, v, \Phi}, c_{p, H}^0, c_{p, L}^0, n_{eff}, i_{2800}^0,$$

$$i_f, T_{c\cdot c}, c_H', S_{c\cdot c}.$$

2. We assign a series of values for p_{exh} in a chosen range of its variation, and for each one of them we carry through the calculation determining the values of the parameters S_a, c_L', T_{exh}, w_{exh}, and P_{sp}.

3. According to the given calculation we construct a graph of the dependence of the parameters T_{exh}, w_{exh} and P_{sp} on the parameter p_{exh}.

For approximately equal conditions, the accuracy of calculation of the parameters T_{exh}, w_{exh} and P_{sp} increases with approach of the value of p_{exh} to 1 atm, since the nomograms for determining the parameter $\Delta i_{L, v, \Phi}$ are constructed precisely for this pressure.

We have broken down the order of carrying out the calculations in certain of the cases most frequently encountered in practice. In the following section we shall present examples of these calculations.

In Example 1 the thermodynamic assessment of a liquid rocket motor is shown, operating on a fuel consisting of four chemical elements: carbon, hydrogen, nitrogen and oxygen.

In Example 2 the calculation is presented for an engine operating on a fuel which does not contain nitrogen, and at a pressure of the combustion products in the combustion chamber of the engine $p_{c \cdot c} =$ $= 50$ atm.

Example 3 shows the method of carrying out the calculations in the case of establishing the relationship between the operating characteristics of an engine and the coefficient of excess oxidant in the fuel.

Examples 4 and 5 show the method of carrying out the calculations for the cases of establishing the relationships between the operating characteristics of an engine and the pressure of the combustion products in the combustion chamber and in the exhaust section of the nozzle of the engine respectively.

15. Examples of Thermodynamic Calculations

EXAMPLE 1. To determine the exhaust velocity and specific thrust for a calculated operating régime of a liquid rocket motor, operating on technical (96 per cent by weight) nitric acid (admixture — water) and kerosene ($C_C = 86{\cdot}8$ per cent; $H_C = 13{\cdot}2$ per cent) for $\alpha_0' = 0{\cdot}8$. The pressure of the combustion products in the combustion chamber is assumed to be $p_{c \cdot c} = 40$ atm, and the pressure in the exhaust section of the nozzle is $p_{exh} = 1$ atm.

1. We determine the content by weight of the chemical elements in 1 kg of oxidant.

The arbitrary chemical formula of the oxidant is

$$HNO_3 + m\, H_2O,$$

where m is the number of moles of water associated with one mole of nitric acid. In the given case, $\xi = 0{\cdot}04$ by weight of admixture — water — is contained in the nitric acid.

Consequently,

$$\frac{\xi}{1-\xi} = \frac{m\mu_{H_2O}}{\mu_{HNO_3}}.$$

Here μ_{H_2O} and μ_{HNO_3} are the molecular weights of water and nitric acid. Obviously,

$$m = \frac{\xi \mu_{HNO_3}}{(1-\xi)\,\mu_{H_2O}} = \frac{0{\cdot}04 \times 63}{0{\cdot}96 \times 18} = 0{\cdot}1459.$$

The arbitrary formula of the oxidant is

$$HNO_3 + 0{\cdot}1459\, H_2O.$$

The arbitrary molecular weight of the oxidant is

$$\mu_0 = \mu_{HNO_3} + 0{\cdot}1459\ \mu_{H_2O};$$
$$\mu_0 = 63 + 0{\cdot}1459 \times 18 = 65{\cdot}627.$$

The content by weight of chemical elements in 1 kg of oxidant, $C_0 = 0$ is:

$$H_o = \frac{1 + 2\times 0{\cdot}1459}{65{\cdot}627} 1000 = 19{\cdot}69\,\text{g};$$

$$N_o = \frac{14}{65{\cdot}627} 1000 = 213{\cdot}2\,\text{g};$$

$$O_o = \frac{(3 + 0{\cdot}1459)\,16}{65{\cdot}627} 1000 = 766{\cdot}5\,\text{g}.$$

2. We determine the weight content of the chemical elements in 1 kg of combustible:

$$C_c = 868\ \text{g};\ H_c = 132\ \text{g};\ N_c = 0;\ O_c = 0.$$

3. The quantity of oxidant theoretically necessary for the oxidation of 1 kg of combustible is found according to formula (3.2):

$$\nu_o = \frac{\frac{8}{3}\times 863 + 8\times 132 - 0}{766{\cdot}3 - \frac{8}{3}\times 0 - 8\times 19{\cdot}69} = 5{\cdot}54\,.$$

We find the value of the excess oxidant coefficient α', corresponding to the given α_0' according to formula (3.3a):

$$\alpha' = \frac{0{\cdot}8\times 5{\cdot}54}{\frac{8}{3}\times 868 + 8(132 + 0{\cdot}8\times 5{\cdot}54\times 19{\cdot}69)};$$
$$\alpha' = 0{\cdot}834.$$

4. We assign a number of values for α: 0·95; 0·90; 0·80; 0·70; and we calculate the value of α_0 for them by formula (3.3).

α	0·95	0·90	0·834	0·80	0·70
α_0	0·939	0·877	0·800	0·761	0·649

An example of the calculation for $\alpha = 0{\cdot}95$ is:

$$\alpha_o = \frac{1}{5{\cdot}54} \frac{\frac{8}{3}\times 868 + 8\times 132 - 0}{\frac{766{\cdot}5}{0{\cdot}95} - 0 - 8\times 19{\cdot}69};$$
$$\alpha_o = 0{\cdot}939.$$

5. The actual weight ratio of oxidant to combustible in the fuel is determined by formula (3.4):

α	0·95	0·90	0·834	0·80	0·70
ν	5·200	4·860	4·432	4·216	3·595

An example of the calculation for $\alpha = 0{\cdot}95$ is:

$$\nu = 0{\cdot}939 \times 5{\cdot}54; \quad \nu = 5{\cdot}200.$$

6. The number of g-atoms of carbon, hydrogen and nitrogen in 1 kg of fuel is determined according to formula (3.5).

α	A_C	A_H	A_N
0·95	11·69	37·82	12·78
0·90	12·35	38·82	12·63
0·834	13·32	40·39	12·46
0·80	13·87	41·22	12·31
0·70	15·77	44·14	11·94

7. We determine the value of the parameter μ^0 by formula (3.6):

α	0·95	0·90	0·834	0·80	0·70
μ°	0·02703	0·02625	0·02517	0·02458	0·02283

An example of the calculation for $\alpha = 0{\cdot}95$ is:

$$\mu^0 = \frac{1}{11{\cdot}69 + 0{\cdot}5(37{\cdot}82 + 12{\cdot}78)};$$

$$\mu^0 = 0{\cdot}02703.$$

8. The independent variables X_C and X_H are determined according to formulae (1.39) and (1.40).

α	X_C	X_H
0·95	12·65	40·90
0·90	12·98	40·78
0·834	13·42	40·65
0·80	13·66	40·60
0·70	14·40	40·32

An example of the calculation for $a = 0{\cdot}95$ is:

$$X_C = 40 \times 0{\cdot}02703 \times 11{\cdot}69 = 12{\cdot}65;$$

$$X_H = 40 \times 0{\cdot}02703 \times 37{\cdot}82 = 40{\cdot}90.$$

9. The following parameters are determined for the chosen values of a by means of the curves in Figs. 1–4, 9–12 and 15–18 in the Appendix.

a	i_v^0	$\Delta i_{H,v,\Phi}$	$\Delta i_{L,v,\Phi}$
0·95	1335	666	14·52
0·90	1462	560	11·87
0·80	1720	393	8·20
0·70	1998	274	5·82

10. We construct a graph of the dependence of the parameters i_v^0, $i_{H,v}$, and $i_{L,v}$, on the excess oxygen coefficient a (Fig. 5).

11. We take from the graph the values of the parameters for the excess oxygen coefficient $a' = 0{\cdot}834$ as found:

$$i_v^0 = 1632;$$

$$i_{H,v} = 438;$$

$$i_{L,v} = 9{\cdot}15.$$

In future we shall carry out the calculation for an excess oxygen coefficient of $a' = 0{\cdot}834$.

12. The value of m_H is determined from the curves in Fig. 7 of the Appendix:

$$m_H = 2{\cdot}881\,.$$

13. We determine $c_{p,H}^0$ according to formula (1.42):

$$c_{p,H}^0 = \frac{1}{40 \times 0{\cdot}02517}\,[356{\cdot}0 + (12{\cdot}454 \times 0{\cdot}834 - 6{\cdot}276) \times 13{\cdot}42 +$$

$$+ (3{\cdot}114 \times 0{\cdot}834 - 1{\cdot}221) \times 40{\cdot}65 -$$

$$- 0{\cdot}797 \log (0{\cdot}834 - 0{\cdot}420) \times 40{\cdot}65] \times 10^{-3}; \quad c_{p,H}^0 = 0{\cdot}4760\,.$$

14. We calculate n_{eff} by formula (2.41):

$$n_{\text{eff}} = 0{\cdot}6242 \log \frac{40 \times 2^{2\cdot881} \times 9{\cdot}15}{438}\,;$$

$$n_{\text{eff}} = 0{\cdot}4925\,.$$

15. We determine i^0_{2800} according to formula (1.41):

$$i^0_{2800} = 1632 \frac{1}{40 \times 0{\cdot}02517} ;$$

$$i^0_{2800} = 1621{\cdot}7 .$$

16. We determine c'_H by formula (2.44), having assumed $p = = p_{c\cdot c} = 40$ atm:

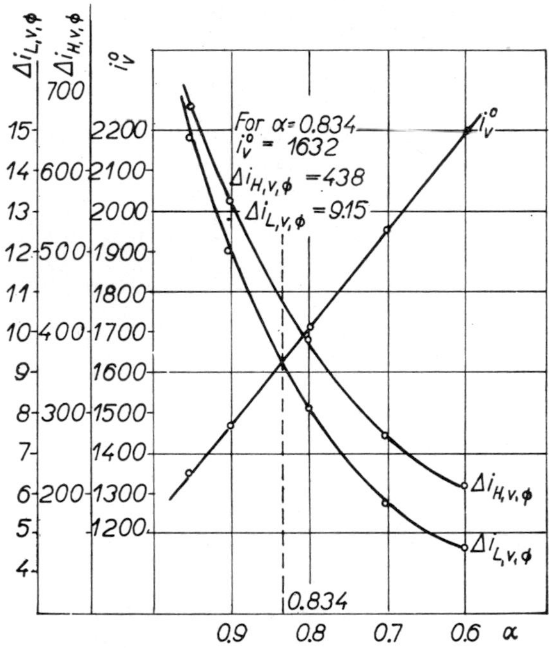

FIG. 5

$$c'_H = \frac{\Delta i_{H,\,v,\,\Phi}}{40\mu^0} \left(\frac{p_{H,\,\Phi}}{p_{c.c}} \right)^{n_{\text{eff}}} .$$

Since $p_{c\cdot c} = 40$ atm and $p_{H,\,\Phi} = 40$ atm, then

$$c'_H = \frac{i_{H,\,v,\,\Phi}}{40\mu^0} = \frac{438}{40 \times 0{\cdot}02517} ,$$

$$c'_H = 435{\cdot}2 .$$

17. The enthalpy of 1 kg of fuel, i_f, is determined according to the method presented in Section 20 of this book.

For $\alpha' = 0{\cdot}834$ the arbitrary formula of the fuel is

$$C_{7\cdot233}\,H_{13\,2} + 6{\cdot}740\ HNO_3 + 0{\cdot}984\ H_2O .$$

The arbitrary molecular weight of the fuel is

$$100 + 424{\cdot}62 + 17{\cdot}71 = 542{\cdot}33\ .$$

The fractions by weight of the fuel components are:

Kerosene $q_{\text{ker}} = \dfrac{100}{542{\cdot}33} = 0{\cdot}1843$ kg;

Water $q_{H_2O} = \dfrac{0{\cdot}984\times18}{542{\cdot}33} = 0{\cdot}0326$ kg;

Nitric acid (100 per cent) $q_{HNO_3} = \dfrac{424{\cdot}62}{542{\cdot}33} = 0{\cdot}7828$ kg.

The enthalpy of the fuel components is determined as a result of solving the examples in Section 20:

$$i_{\text{ker}} = 10{,}399 \text{ kcal/kg}\ ;$$

$$i_{H_2O\ (\text{liquid})} = -459 \text{ kcal/kg}\ ;$$

$$i_{HNO_3} = -128 \text{ kcal/kg}\ .$$

The heat of solution of water in nitric acid should also be taken into account (with a negative sign), equal to approximately 12·6 kcal/kg of nitric acid. Taking into account the heat of solution, the enthalpy of the nitric acid will be equal to:

$$i_{HNO_3} = -128 - 12{\cdot}6 = -140{\cdot}6 \text{ kcal/kg}.$$

The enthalpy of 1 kg of fuel is:

$$i_f = i_{\text{ker}}\, q_{\text{ker}} + i_{HNO_3}\, q_{HNO_3} + i_{H_2O}\, q_{H_2O}\ ;$$

$$i_f = 10{\cdot}399 \times 0{\cdot}1843 - 140{\cdot}6 \times 0{\cdot}7828 - 459 \times 0{\cdot}0326\ :$$

$$i_f = 1791{\cdot}9 \text{ kcal/kg}\ .$$

18. We determine i_k by formula (3.7) :

$$i_k = 1791{\cdot}9 - 1621{\cdot}7 + 0{\cdot}4760 \times 2800\ ;$$

$$i_k = 1504{\cdot}2\ .$$

19. The temperature of the combustion products in the combustion chamber of the engine $T_{c\cdot c}$ is determined by means of equation (3.8).

We assign a number of values for T_{ki}, close to the expected $T_{c\cdot c}$, and from the condition that $i_{ki} = i_k$ we determine $T_{c\cdot c}$. We carry out the calculations with the aid of a table of the following form (only one of the concluding lines of the calculation is shown in the table) .

T_{ki}	$\frac{T_{ki}-2200}{1200}$	log [2]	m_{H} [3]	log c'_{H}	log Δi_{ki} = = [4] + [5]	Δi_{ki}	$c^0_{p,\,\mathrm{H}}T_{ki}$	i_{ki} = = [7] + [8]
2940	0·6164	$\bar{1}$·7900 —0·2100	—0·6048	2·6388	2·034	108·1	1399·0	1507·1

$T_{\text{c·c}} = 2940°\text{K}$, since $i_{ki} \approx i_k$.

20. The entropy of the combustion products $S_{\text{c·c}}$ in the combustion chamber of the engine is determined by equation (3.9).

Since $c'_H \left(\frac{T_{\text{c.c}} - 2200}{1200}\right)^{m_H} = \Delta i_{\text{c·c}} = 108{\cdot}1$ (see the seventh column of the table), then

$$S_{\text{c·c}} = 2{\cdot}303 \times 0{\cdot}4760 \log \frac{2940}{2800} - \frac{0{\cdot}004574}{0{\cdot}02517} \log 40 +$$

$$+ 108{\cdot}1 \left(\frac{1}{2940} + \frac{1{\cdot}527 \times 10^{-5}}{0{\cdot}4925}\right)$$

$$S_{\text{c·c}} = -0{\cdot}2261.$$

21. The parameter $c^0_{p,\,L}$ is determined according to formula (1.43):

$$c^0_{p,\,L} = \frac{1}{40 \times 0{\cdot}02517}\,[349{\cdot}6 + (12{\cdot}152 \times 0{\cdot}834 - 6{\cdot}022)\,13{\cdot}42 +$$

$$+ (3{\cdot}038 \times 0{\cdot}834 - 1{\cdot}336)\,40{\cdot}65 - 0{\cdot}825 \log (0{\cdot}834 - 0{\cdot}42)\,40{\cdot}65] \times$$

$$\times 10^{-3};$$

$$c^0_{p,\,L} = 0{\cdot}4630.$$

22. The parameter m_L is determined from the curves in Fig. 8 of the Appendix:

$$m_L = 5{\cdot}727.$$

23. We determine S_a according to formula (3.11), taking into account the fact that $p_{\text{exh}} = 1$ atm:

$$S_a = -0{\cdot}2261 - 2{\cdot}303 \times 0{\cdot}4630 \times \log 2800;$$

$$S_a = 3{\cdot}4489.$$

24. We determine the temperature of the combustion products in the exhaust section of the nozzle T_{exh}. Since in the given case

$$\frac{S_a}{c^0_{p,\,L}} = \frac{3{\cdot}4489}{0{\cdot}4630} = 7{\cdot}44 < 750,$$

then equation (3.12) cannot be used for determining the temperature, but the calculation is carried out according to formula (3.13):

$$\log T_{\text{exh}} = \frac{3{\cdot}4489}{2{\cdot}303 \times 0{\cdot}4630} = 3{\cdot}239\,;$$

$$T_{\text{exh}} = 1707^{\circ}\text{K}\,.$$

25. The enthalpy of the combustion products in the exhaust section of the nozzle is determined from equation (2.51). For this

$$c_L'\left(\frac{T_{\text{exh}} - 1400}{1400}\right)^{m_L} = \Delta i_{\text{exh}} = 0\,;$$

$$i_{\text{exh}} = 1621{\cdot}7 + 0{\cdot}4630\,(1707 - 2800) + 0\,;$$

$$i_{\text{exh}} = 1115{\cdot}7 \text{ kcal/kg}\,.$$

26. The theoretical ideal exhaust velocity of the combustion products is determined from equation (3.14) :

$$w_{\text{exh}} = 91.55\sqrt{(1791{\cdot}9 - 1115{\cdot}7)}\,;$$

$$w_{\text{exh}} = 2382 \text{ m/sec.}$$

27. The specific thrust at the calculated operating régime of the engine is equal to

$$P_{\text{sp}} = \frac{2382}{9{\cdot}81}\,;$$

$$P_{\text{sp}} = 242{\cdot}8 \text{ kg}\cdot\text{sec/kg.}$$

28. The results of the calculation are presented in a graph in Fig. 7 (see the points corresponding to $a = 0{\cdot}834$).

EXAMPLE 2. To carry out the calculation of the exhaust velocity and specific thrust at a calculated operating régime of an engine operating on 95 per cent by weight ethyl alcohol (admixture – water) for an excess oxidant coefficient $a_0' = 0{\cdot}7$ ($a' = 0{\cdot}748$). The pressure of the combustion products in the combustion chamber of the engine is $p_{\text{c·c}} = 50$ atm, the pressure of the combustion products at the nozzle exit is $p_{\text{exh}} = 1$ atm.

For the given fuel there is an entropy diagram, which enables a comparison to be made between the results of the calculations obtained by the proposed method and from the diagram.

1. We find the content by weight of the chemical elements in 1 kg of combustible. The arbitrary chemical formula of the combustible is

$$C_2H_5OH + m\,H_2O\,,$$

where m is the number of moles of water associated with one mole of ethyl alcohol.

In the ethyl alcohol in the given case, $\xi = 0{\cdot}05$ by weight of the admixture — water — is contained. Consequently,

$$\frac{\xi}{1-\xi} = \frac{m\mu_{H_2O}}{\mu_{C_2H_5OH}} .$$

Here μ_{H_2O} and $\mu_{C_2H_5OH}$ are the molecular weights of water and ethyl alcohol.

It is obvious that

$$m = \frac{\xi\mu_{C_2H_5OH}}{(1-\xi)\,\mu_{H_2O}} = \frac{0{\cdot}05\times 46}{0{\cdot}95\times 18} ;$$

$$m = 0{\cdot}1345 .$$

The arbitrary formula of the combustible is

$$C_2H_5OH + 0{\cdot}1345\ H_2O .$$

The arbitrary molecular weight of the combustible is

$$\mu_c = \mu_{C_2H_5OH} + 0{\cdot}1345\ \mu_{H_2O} ;$$

$$\mu_c = 46 + 0{\cdot}1345 \times 18 = 48{\cdot}422 .$$

The content by weight of the chemical elements in 1 kg of combustible is

$$C_c = \frac{2\times 12}{48{\cdot}422}\times 1000 = 495{\cdot}7\ \text{g} ;$$

$$H_c = \frac{6 + 0{\cdot}1345\times 2}{48{\cdot}422}\times 1000 = 129{\cdot}5\ \text{g} ;$$

$$N_c = 0 ;$$

$$O_c = \frac{(1 + 0{\cdot}1345)\times 16}{48{\cdot}422}\times 1000 = 375{\cdot}0\ \text{g} .$$

2. The content by weight of the chemical elements in 1 kg of oxidant is:

$$C_o = 0 ;$$

$$H_o = 0 ;$$

$$O_o = 1000\ \text{g} ;$$

$$N_o = 0 .$$

3. We assign a series of values for α: 0·95; 0·90; 0·80; 0·70; 0·60; 0·55; and we carry out the calculation of the independent parameters X_C and X_H for these values and also for $\alpha' = 0{\cdot}748$.

In the given example, it is not necessary to carry out a preliminary determination of the parameters ν_0, ν, A_C, A_H and μ^0 in order to calculate the values of X_C and X_H, since more simple expressions can be found for X_C and X_H. Actually, since in the given case

$$C_o = H_o = N_c = N_o = 0\,,$$

then

$$A_C = \frac{C_c}{12(1+\nu)}; \quad A_H = \frac{H_c}{1+\nu};$$

$$\mu^0 = \frac{1}{A_C + 0{\cdot}5\,A_H} = \frac{12(1+\nu)}{C_c + 6H_c}.$$

Consequently, independently of the values chosen for a, the parameters X_C and X_H are determined by the expressions

$$X_C = 40\mu^0 A_C = \frac{40\,C_c}{C_c + 6H_c} = \frac{40\times495{\cdot}7}{495{\cdot}7 + 6\times129{\cdot}5} = 15{\cdot}59\,;$$

$$X_C = 40\mu^0 A_H = \frac{40\times12H_c}{C_c + 6H_c} = \frac{40\times129{\cdot}5\times12}{495{\cdot}7 + 6\times129{\cdot}5} = 48{\cdot}83\,.$$

4. The parameters i_v^0, $\Delta i_{H,v,\Phi}$, and $\Delta i_{L,v,\Phi}$ are determined for the chosen values or a by the curves in Figs. 1–6 and 9–20 of the Appendix.

a	i_v^0	$i_{H,v\,\Phi}$	$i_{L,v,\Phi}$
0·95	1430	744	16·12
0·90	1575	607	13·02
0·80	1861	415	8·70
0·70	2148	287	6·15
0·60	2429	227	5·10
0·55	2578	214	4·77

5. We construct a graph of the dependence of the parameters i_v^0, $\Delta i_{H,v,\Phi}$ and $\Delta i_{L,v,\Phi}$ on the excess oxygen coefficient a (Fig. 6).

6. We take from the graph the values of the parameters for the given excess oxygen coefficient $a' = 0{\cdot}748$:

$$i_v^0 = 2010\,;$$

$$\Delta i_{H,v,\Phi} = 342\,;$$

$$\Delta i_{L,v,\Phi} = 7{\cdot}13\,.$$

In future, we shall carry out the calculation only for an excess oxygen coefficient of $a' = 0{\cdot}748$.

7. The theoretical quantity of oxidant necessary for the oxidation of 1 kg of combustible is determined according to formula (3.2):

$$\nu_0 = \frac{\frac{8}{3}\,495{\cdot}7 + 8 \times 129{\cdot}5 - 375{\cdot}0}{1000}\,;$$

$$\nu_o = 1{\cdot}983\,.$$

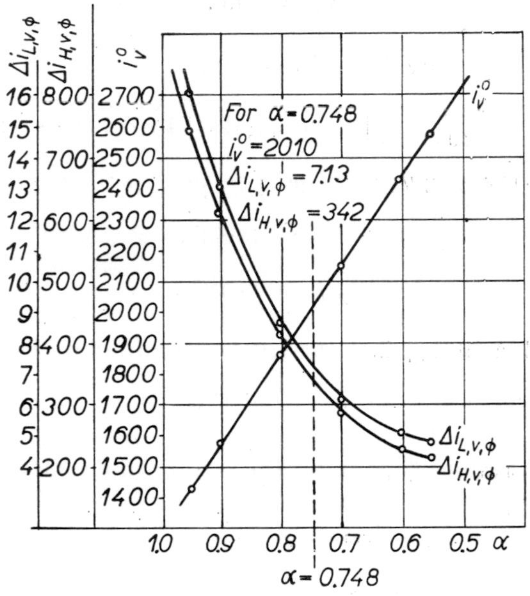

FIG. 6

8. The actual weight ratio of the fuel components is determined by formula (3.4):

$$\nu = 0{\cdot}70 \times 1{\cdot}983\,;$$

$$\nu = 1{\cdot}390.$$

9. The number of g-atoms of carbon and hydrogen in 1 kg of fuel is determined according to formula (3.5):

$$A_{\mathrm{C}} = \frac{495{\cdot}7}{12\,(1 + 1{\cdot}39)} = 17{\cdot}30\,;$$

$$A_{\mathrm{H}} = \frac{129{\cdot}5}{1 + 1{\cdot}39} = 54{\cdot}24.$$

10. We determine the value of the parameter μ^0 by formula (3.6) :

$$\mu^0 = \frac{1}{17{\cdot}30 + 0{\cdot}5 \times 54{\cdot}24};$$

$$\mu^0 = 0{\cdot}02252.$$

11. m_H is determined by the curves in Fig. 7 of the Appendix :

$$m_H = 2{\cdot}96\,.$$

12. We find $c^0_{p,H}$ by formula (1.42) :

$$c^0_{p,H} = \frac{1}{40 \times 0{\cdot}02252}\,[356{\cdot}0 + (12{\cdot}454 \times 0{\cdot}748 - 6{\cdot}276) \times$$

$$\times\, 15{\cdot}59 + (3{\cdot}114 \times 0{\cdot}748 - 1{\cdot}221)\, 48{\cdot}83 - 0{\cdot}797 \log (0{\cdot}748 -$$

$$- 0{\cdot}420) \times 48{\cdot}83]\, 10^{-3};$$

$$c^0_{p,H} = 0{\cdot}5297\,.$$

13. The value of n_{eff} is calculated according to formula (2.41) :

$$n_{\text{eff}} = 0{\cdot}507\,.$$

14. We determine i^0_{2800} according to formula (1.41) :

$$i^0_{2800} = \frac{2010}{40 \times 0{\cdot}02252};$$

$$i^0_{2800} = 2232 \text{ kcal/kg}.$$

15. We determine c'_H by formula (2.44), assuming that

$$p = p_{\text{c·c}} = 50 \text{ atm};$$

$$c'_H = \frac{342}{40 \times 0{\cdot}02252} \left(\frac{40}{50}\right)^{0{\cdot}507};$$

$$c'_H = 339{\cdot}2\,.$$

16. In accordance with the method presented in Section 20, we find the enthalpy of 1 kg of fuel i_f.

For $\alpha' = 0{\cdot}748$, the arbitrary formula of the fuel is

$$C_2H_5OH + 0{\cdot}1345\, H_2O + 2{\cdot}1\, O_2\,.$$

The arbitrary molecular weight of the fuel is

$$46 + 0{\cdot}1345 \times 18 + 2{\cdot}1 \times 32 = 115{\cdot}62\,.$$

The weight ratio of the fuel components is:
alcohol (100%) :

$$q_{C_2H_5OH} = \frac{46}{115 \cdot 62} = 0 \cdot 3975 \text{ kg};$$

water

$$q_{H_2O} = \frac{0 \cdot 1345 \times 18}{115 \cdot 62} = 0 \cdot 0209 \text{ kg};$$

oxygen

$$q_{O_2} = \frac{2 \cdot 1 \times 32}{115 \cdot 62} = 0 \cdot 5818 \text{ kg}.$$

The enthalpy of the ethyl alcohol is determined by separate calculation from the known value of the heat of combustion

$$Q_{comb} = 326 \text{ kcal/mole}.$$

The equation for the combustion of alcohol in oxygen for $\alpha_0 = 1$ is

$$C_2H_5OH + 3\,O_2 = 2CO_2 + 3H_2O.$$

According to formula (2) Section 20

$$i_{C_2H_5OH} = Q_{comb} - 3I_{O_2} + 2I_{CO_2} + 3I_{H_2O\,(liquid)}.$$

According to Table 1 of the Appendix, at normal conditions (+20 °C)

$$I_{O_2} = 2 \cdot 03 \text{ kcal/mole};$$

$$I_{CO_2} = 2 \cdot 18 \text{ kcal/mole}.$$

The enthalpy of liquid water is determined in Section 20:

$$I_{H_2O\,(liquid)} = -8 \cdot 26 \text{ kcal/mole} = -459 \text{ kcal/kg}.$$

Consequently, the enthalpy of the alcohol is equal to :

$$i_{C_2H_5OH} = 326 - 3 \times 2 \cdot 03 + 2 \times 2 \cdot 18 + 3(-8 \cdot 26):$$

$$i_{C_2H_5OH} = 299 \cdot 6 \text{ kcal/mole} = 6510 \text{ kcal/kg}.$$

The enthalpy of liquid oxygen at the boiling-point at atmospheric pressure can be found by subtracting from the enthalpy of oxygen gas (at —183°C) the heat of vaporization.

The enthalpy of oxygen gas at —183°C is equal to 0·63 kcal/mole.

The heat of vaporization of oxygen is

$$Q_{vap} = 1 \cdot 63 \text{ kcal/mole}.$$

The enthalpy of liquid oxygen is

$$i_{O_2\,(\text{liquid})} = 0{\cdot}63 - 1{\cdot}63 = -1{\cdot}00 \ \text{kcal/mole} ;$$

$$i_{O_2\,(\text{liquid})} = -31{\cdot}25 \ \text{kcal/kg} .$$

We now determine the enthalpy of 1 kg of fuel :

$$i_f = 0{\cdot}3975 \times 6510 + 0{\cdot}0209(-459) + 0{\cdot}5818(-31{\cdot}25) ;$$

$$i_f = 2559 \ \text{kcal/kg} .$$

17. We determine i_k according to formula (3.7) :

$$i_k = 2559 - 2232 + 0{\cdot}5297 \times 2800 ;$$

$$i_k = 1810.$$

18. The temperature of the combustion products in the combustion chamber is determined by equation (3.8) according to the method proposed in Section 9. The final result of the calculations for determining the value of the temperature $T_{c{\cdot}c}$ is set out in the table. The value of the temperature $T_{c{\cdot}c}$ is determined from the condition $i_{ki} = i_k$

$$T_{c{\cdot}c} = 3120°\text{K}$$

T_{ki}	$\frac{T_{ki} - 2200}{1200}$	log [2]	m_H [3]	log c'_H	log Δi_{ki} = = [4] + [5]	Δi_{ki}	$C^0_{p,\,H} T_{ki}$	i_{ki} = = [7] + [8]
3120	0·7670	$\bar{1}{\cdot}8848$	−0·341	2·5305	2·1895	154·7	1652	1806·7

19. The enthalpy of the combustion products in the combustion chamber of the engine is determined according to equation (3.9). Since

$$c'_H \left(\frac{T_{c.c} - 2200}{1200} \right)^{m_H} = \Delta i_{c{\cdot}c} = 154{\cdot}7$$

(see column seven of table), then

$$S_{c{\cdot}c} = 2{\cdot}303 \times 0{\cdot}5297 \log \frac{3210}{2800} = \frac{0{\cdot}004574}{0{\cdot}02252} \log 50 + 154{\cdot}7 \left(\frac{1}{3120} + \right.$$

$$\left. + \frac{1{\cdot}527 \times 10^{-5}}{0{\cdot}507} \right) ;$$

$$S_{c{\cdot}c} = -0{\cdot}2295 .$$

20. The parameter $c^0_{p,L}$ is determined by formula (1.43) :

$$c^0_{p,L} = \frac{1}{40 \times 0{\cdot}02252} [349{\cdot}6 + (12{\cdot}152 \times 0{\cdot}748 - 6{\cdot}022)\, 15{\cdot}59 +$$

$$+ (3{\cdot}038 \times 0{\cdot}748 - 1{\cdot}336)\, 48{\cdot}83 - 0{\cdot}825 \log (0{\cdot}748 - 0{\cdot}42)\, 48{\cdot}83]$$

$$\times 10^{-3} ;$$

$$c^0_{p,L} = 0{\cdot}5142 .$$

21. We determine the parameter m_L from the nomogram in Fig. 8 of the Appendix:

$$m_L = 5{\cdot}78 .$$

22. We find S_a from formula (3.11) :
Since $p_{\text{exh}} = 1$ atm, then

$$S_a = -0{\cdot}2295 + 2{\cdot}303 \times 0{\cdot}5142 \times \log 2800 ;$$

$$S_a = 3{\cdot}8525 .$$

23. Since in the given case

$$\frac{S_a}{c^0_{p,L}} = \frac{3{\cdot}8525}{0{\cdot}5142} < 7{\cdot}50 ,$$

then the calculation of the temperature of the combustion products T_{exh} can be carried out by the simplified method, using formula (3.13) :

$$\log T_{\text{exh}} = \frac{3{\cdot}8525}{2{\cdot}303 \times 0{\cdot}5142} = 3{\cdot}251 ;$$

$$T_{\text{exh}} = 1780^\circ\text{K}.$$

24. The enthalpy of the combustion products in the exhaust section of the nozzle is determined according to equation (2.51). For this

$$c'_L \left(\frac{T_{\text{exh}} - 1400}{1400}\right)^{m_L} = \Delta i_{\text{exh}} = 0 ;$$

$$i_{\text{exh}} = 2232 + 0{\cdot}5142\,(1780 - 2800) + 0 ;$$

$$i_{\text{exh}} = 1707 \text{ kcal/kg} .$$

25. The theoretical ideal exhaust velocity of the combustion products from the engine is determined by equation (3.14) :

$$w_{\text{exh}} = 91{\cdot}53 \sqrt{(2559 - 1707)} ;$$

$$w_{\text{exh}} = 2673 \text{ m/sec.}$$

26. The specific thrust for the calculated operating régime of the engine is equal to

$$P_{sp} = \frac{2673}{9 \cdot 81};$$

$$P_{sp} = 272 \cdot 5 \text{ kg} \cdot \text{sec/kg}.$$

The results of calculation can be compared with those given by the entropy diagram (see [7]).

	$T_{c.c}$ °K	T_{exh} °K	w_{exh}, m/sec	P_{sp}, $\frac{\text{kg}\cdot\text{sec}}{\text{kg}}$	Error in the value of specific thrust, %
Calculation	3120	1780	2673	272·5	0·4
Diagram ...	3125	1780	2683	273·7	

The calculation is carried out on a 50-cm logarithmic slide-rule by one calculator over a working time of 3 hr.

EXAMPLE 3. To establish for the components of the fuel given in Example 1, the dependence of specific thrust and temperature of the combustion products in the combustion chamber and in the exhaust section of the engine nozzle on the excess oxidant coefficient (within the range of values of a from 0·95 to 0·70). The pressure of the combustion products in the combustion chamber $p_{c \cdot c} = 40$ atm, and in the exhaust section of the nozzle $p_{exh} = 1$ atm.

We shall carry out the calculation for values of an excess oxygen factor a equal to : 0·95; 0·90; 0·80; 0·70 . The initial portion of the calculation (up to part 9) is completely identical with the calculations carried out in Example 1. We shall then carry out the calculation according to the scheme described in Section 14A.

1. We find the parameters m_H and m_L from the nomogram of Figs. 7 and 8 of the Appendix.

a	m_H	m_L
0·95	2·870	5·71
0·90	2·875	5·72
0·80	2·884	5·73
0·70	2·892	5·74

2. The enthalpy of the combustible and of the oxidant were determined in part 17 of Example 1. Having calculated the weight ratios

of combustible and oxidant, q_f and q_o, in 1 kg of fuel, we find the enthalpy of 1 kg of fuel according to formula (1) of Section 20 for the chosen values of a. The results of the calculations are presented in the table :

a	q_{ker} kg/kg	q_{HNO_3} kg/kg	q_{H_2O} kg/kg	i_f $\frac{\text{kcal}}{\text{kg}}$
0·95	0·1615	0·8045	0·0340	1550·3
0·90	0·1710	0·7960	0·0332	1650·9
0·80	0·1921	0·7760	0·0323	1873·1
0·70	0·2180	0·7510	0·0313	2148·1

3. We determine $c^0_{p,H}$ by formula (1.42).

a_0	0·95	0·90	0·80	0·70
$c^0_{p,H}$ ..	0·4683	0·4712	0·4796	0·4899

An example of the calculation for $a = 0{\cdot}95$ is :

$$c^0_{p,H} = \frac{1}{40\times 0{\cdot}02703}\,[356{\cdot}0 + (12{\cdot}454\times 0{\cdot}95 - 6{\cdot}276)\,12{\cdot}65 + (3{\cdot}114\times 0{\cdot}95 - 1{\cdot}221)\,40{\cdot}90 - 0{\cdot}797\log(0{\cdot}95 - 0{\cdot}42)\times 40{\cdot}90]\,10^{-3};$$

$$c^0_{p,H} = 0{\cdot}4683\,.$$

4. We determine $c^0_{p,L}$ according to formula (1.43).

a	0·95	0·90	0·80	0·70
$c^0_{p,L}$ ...	0·4552	0·4582	0·4663	0·4767

An example of the calculation for $a = 0{\cdot}95$ is :

$$c^0_{p,L} = \frac{1}{40\times 0{\cdot}02703}\,[349{\cdot}6 + (12{\cdot}152\times 0{\cdot}95 - 6{\cdot}022)\,12{\cdot}65 + (3{\cdot}038\times 0{\cdot}95 - 1{\cdot}336)\,40{\cdot}90 - 0{\cdot}825\log(0{\cdot}95 - 0{\cdot}42)\times 40{\cdot}90]\,10^{-3};$$

$$c^0_{p,H} = 0{\cdot}4552\,.$$

5. We find i^0_{2800} from formula (1.41).

α	0·95	0·90	0·80	0·70
i^0_{2800}	1234·9	1392·8	1749·2	2188·2

An example of the calculation for $\alpha = 0{\cdot}95$ is :

$$i^0_{2800} = 1335 \frac{1}{40 \times 0{\cdot}02703} ;$$

$$i^0_{2800} = 1234{\cdot}9$$

6. i_k is determined by formula (3.7).

α	0·95	0·90	0·80	0·70
i_k	1625·9	1577·4	1466·8	1331·6

An example of the calculation for $\alpha = 0{\cdot}95$ is :

$$i_k = 1550{\cdot}3 - 1234{\cdot}9 + 2800 \times 0{\cdot}4683 ;$$

$$i_k = 1625{\cdot}9 .$$

7. We find n_{eff} according to formula (2.41).

α	0·95	0·90	0·80	0·70
n_{eff}	0·5022	0·4947	0·4927	0·4994

An example of the calculation for $\alpha = 0{\cdot}95$ is :

$$n_{\text{eff}} = 0{\cdot}6242 \log \frac{40 \times 2^{2{\cdot}87} \times 14{\cdot}52}{666} ;$$

$$n_{\text{eff}} = 0{\cdot}5022 .$$

8. c'_H is determined according to formula (2.44).

α	0·95	0·90	0·80	0·70
c'_H	616·0	533·5	400·0	300·0

An example of the calculation for $a = 0{\cdot}95$ is :

$$c'_H = \frac{\Delta i_{H,v,\Phi}}{40\mu^0}\left(\frac{p_{H,\Phi}}{p_{c,c}}\right)^{n_{\text{eff}}}$$

or, since $p_{c\cdot c} = 40$ atm and $p_{H,\Phi} = 40$ atm,

$$c'_H = \frac{666}{40\times 0{\cdot}02703} = 616{\cdot}0.$$

The temperature of the combustion products in the combustion chamber of the engine is determined according to equation (3.8) by the method set forth in Section 9.

The final results of the calculations for the chosen values of a are presented in a table :

T_{ki}	$\frac{T_{ki}-2200}{1200}$	log [2]	m_H [3]	log c'_H	log Δi_{ki} = [4] + [5]	Δi_{ki}	$c^0_{p,H}\, T_{ki}$	i_{ki} = [7] + [8]
3023	0·6860	$\bar{1}{\cdot}8363$ $-0{\cdot}1637$	−0·4700	2·7896	2·3196	208·8	1416	1625
2998	0·6650	$\bar{1}{\cdot}8230$ $-0{\cdot}1770$	−0·5088	2·7272	2·2184	165·4	1413	1578
2890	0·5747	$\bar{1}{\cdot}7596$ $-0{\cdot}2404$	−0·6934	2·6020	1·9086	81·0	1386	1467
2670	0·3915	$\bar{1}{\cdot}5930$ $-0{\cdot}4070$	−1·177	2·4770	1·3000	20·0	1308	1328

Consequently, for $i_{ki} = i_k$, the temperature $T_{c\cdot c}$ is equal to

a	0·95	0·90	0·80	0·70
$T_{c.c}$ °K ..	3023	2998	2890	2670

9. We compute $S_{c\cdot c}$ according to equation (3.9).

a	0·95	0·90	0·80	0·70
$S_{c.c}$	−0·1602	−0·1869	−0·2524	−0·3354

An example of the calculation for $a = 0{\cdot}95$ is :

$$S_{c\cdot c} = 2{\cdot}303 \times 0{\cdot}4683 \log \frac{3023}{2800} - \frac{0{\cdot}004574}{0{\cdot}02703} \log 40 + $$
$$+ 208{\cdot}8 \left(\frac{1}{3023} + \frac{1{\cdot}527 \times 10^{-5}}{0{\cdot}5022}\right);$$
$$S_{c\cdot c} = -0{\cdot}1602 .$$

10. S_a is determined by formula (3.11), taking into account that $p_{exh} = 1$ atm .

a	0·95	0·90	0·80	0·70
S_a	3·4528	3·4501	3·4498	3·4496

An example of the calculation for $a = 0{\cdot}95$ is :

$$S_a = -0{\cdot}1602 + 0{\cdot}4552 \times 2{\cdot}303 \log 2800 ;$$
$$S_a = 3{\cdot}4528 .$$

11. We determine c'_L according to formula (2.49), taking into account that $p_{L,\Phi} = 1$ atm, and $p_{exb} = 1$ atm .

a	0·95	0·90	0·80	0·70
c'_L	537·2	439·0	303·5	215·0

An example of the calculation for $a = 0{\cdot}95$ is :

$$c'_L = \frac{14{\cdot}52}{0{\cdot}02703} ;$$
$$c'_L = 537{\cdot}2 .$$

12. We find the temperature of the combustion products in the exhaust section of the nozzle by equation (3.12) for an excess oxygen coefficient $a = 0{\cdot}95$.

The final results of the calculation are given in the table:

$T_{exh\ i}$	$\frac{T_{exh\ i} - 1400}{1400}$	log [2]	m_L [3]	log c'_L	log $\Delta i_{exh\ i}$ = = [4] + [5]
1964	0·403	$\bar{1}{\cdot}6054$ —0.3946	—2·2540	2·730	0·476

$\Delta i_{exh\ i}$	$\frac{1}{T_{exh\ i}} + \frac{1.527\times 10^{-5}}{n_{eff}}$	$\boxed{7}\cdot\boxed{8}$	$2.303\ c^{0}_{p,L} \log T_{exh\ i}$	$S_{ai} = \boxed{9} + \boxed{10}$
2·99	0·000539	0·0016	3·4513	3·4529

Consequently, since $S_{ai} \approx S_a$, the temperature of the combustion products in the exhaust section of the nozzle for $a = 0{\cdot}95$ is equal to 1964°K. For the remaining values of the excess oxygen coefficient the calculation of T_{exh} is handled by formula (3.13). Finally, we obtain the following data :

a	0·95	0·90	0·80	0·70
T_{exh} °K ..	1964	1861	1631	1387

13. The enthalpy of the combustion products in the exhaust section of the nozzle is determined according to equation (2.51).

a	0·95	0·90	0·80	0·70
i_{exh}	857·4	962·6	1204·2	1514·2

An example of the calculation for $a = 0{\cdot}95$ is :

$$i_{exh} = 1234{\cdot}9 + 0{\cdot}4552\,(1964 - 2800) + 3{\cdot}0\,;$$

$$i_{exh} = 857{\cdot}4 \ \text{kcal/kg}\,.$$

14. The specific thrust.

a	0·95	0·90	0·80	0·70
P_{sp}	245·6	245·0	241·7	235·0

An example of the calculation for $a = 0{\cdot}95$ is :

$$P_{sp} = 9{\cdot}33 \sqrt{(1550{\cdot}3 - 857{\cdot}4)}\,;$$

$$P_{sp} = 245{\cdot}6 \ \text{kg}\cdot\text{sec/kg}\,.$$

The results of the calculations are presented graphically in Fig. 7 in the form of the dependence of the unknown values on the excess oxygen coefficient and on the excess oxidant coefficient.

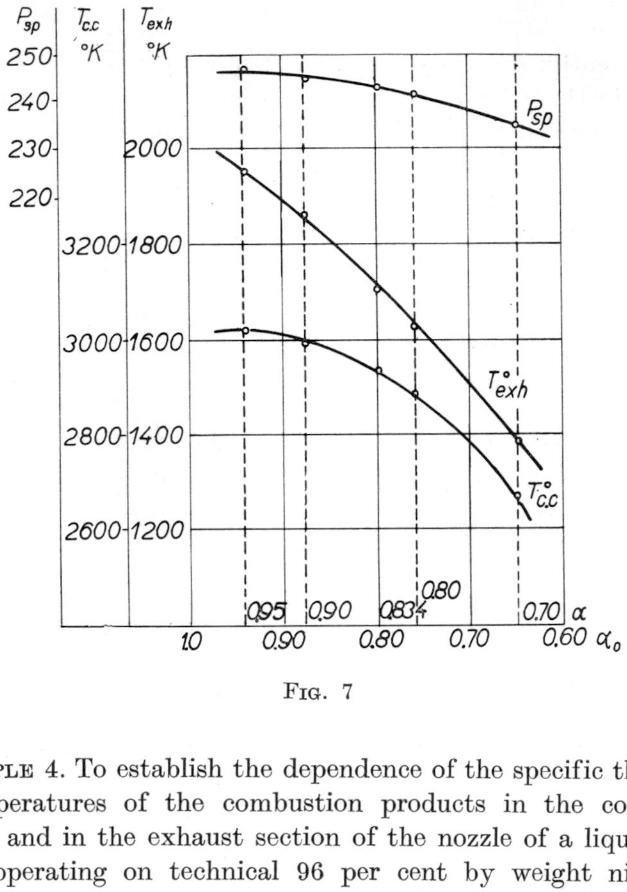

FIG. 7

EXAMPLE 4. To establish the dependence of the specific thrust and the temperatures of the combustion products in the combustion chamber and in the exhaust section of the nozzle of a liquid rocket engine, operating on technical 96 per cent by weight nitric acid (admixture — water) and kerosene ($C_c = 86{\cdot}8$ per cent ; $H_c = 13{\cdot}2$ per cent), on the pressure of the combustion products in the combustion chamber $p_{c{\cdot}c}$ within the range 20–100 atm .

The excess oxidant coefficient is $\alpha_0' = 0{\cdot}8$ ($\alpha' = 0{\cdot}834$), the pressure of the combustion products in the exhaust section of the nozzle is $p_{\text{exh}} = 1$ atm.

It can be seen from the conditions of the problem that the composition of the fuel components and the excess oxidant coefficient in this example coincide completely with the corresponding parameters in Example 1. The initial portions of the calculation (up to part 15) are identical with the calculations presented in Example 1. We shall carry out the calculation further in accordance with the scheme described in Section 14B.

We assign a number of values for $p_{c\cdot c}$ (20; 40; 60; 80; 100 atm) and for each one of them we shall carry out the following calculations.

1. We determine c'_H according to formula (2.44).

$p_{c\cdot c}$	20	40	60	80	100
c'_H	612·3	435·2	352.5	309·4	277·2

An example of the calculation for $p_{c\cdot c} = 20$ atm is :

$$c'_H = \frac{438}{40\times0{\cdot}02517}\left(\frac{40}{20}\right)^{0\cdot4925};$$

$$c'_H = 612{\cdot}3\ .$$

2. The temperature of the combustion products in the combustion chamber $T_{c\cdot c}$ is determined by equation (3.8). We recall that $i_k =$ $= 1504{\cdot}2$.

In order to calculate the temperature $T_{c\cdot c}$ for each one of the chosen values of the pressure $p_{c\cdot c}$, we assign a number of values for the temperature T_{ki} , close to the expected value of $T_{c\cdot c}$, and from the condition $i_{ki} = i_k$ we determine $T_{c\cdot c}$.

The final results of the calculations are presented in a table.

T_{ki} °K	$\frac{T_{ki} - 2200}{1200}$	log [2]	m_H [3]	log c'_H [4]	log Δi_{ki} = [3] + [4]	i_{ki}	$c^0_{p\,H} T_{ki}$	i_{ki} = [7] + [8]
2895	0·5790	$\bar{1}$·7630 −0·2370	−0·6825	2·7870	2·1045	127·2	1377	1504·2
2940	0·6164	$\bar{1}$·7900 −0·2100	−0·6048	2·6388	2·0340	108·1	1399	1507·1
2963	0·6360	$\bar{1}$·8035 −0·1965	−0·5660	2·5472	1·9812	95·7	1410	1505·7
2977	0·6474	$\bar{1}$·8120 −0·1880	−0·5413	2·4905	1·9492	89·0	1417	1506·0
2987	0·6560	$\bar{1}$·8170 −0·1830	−0·5272	2·4430	1·9158	82·3	1421	1503·3

Thus,

$p_{c.c}$	20	40	60	80	100
$T_{c.c}$ °K	2895	2940	2963	2977	2987

3. We determine $S_{c\cdot c}$ according to equation (3.9).

$p_{c.c}$	20	40	60	80	100
$S_{c.c}$	— 0·1688	— 0·2261	— 0·2560	— 0·2790	— 0·2986

An example of the calculation for $p_{c\cdot c} = 20$ atm is :

$$S_{c\cdot c} = 2{\cdot}305 \times 0{\cdot}4760 \log \frac{2895}{2800} - \frac{0{\cdot}004574}{0{\cdot}02517} \log 20 +$$

$$+ 127{\cdot}2 \left(\frac{1}{2895} + \frac{1{\cdot}527 \times 10^{-5}}{0{\cdot}4925} \right);$$

$$S_{c\cdot c} = -0{\cdot}1688\ .$$

4. We determine S_a by formula (3.11).

$p_{c.c}$	20	40	60	80	100
S_a	3·5062	3·4489	3·4190	3·3960	3·3764

An example of the calculation for $p_{c\cdot c} = 20$ atm is :

Since $p_{exh} = 1$ atm, then

$$S_a = -0{\cdot}1688 + 2{\cdot}303 \times 0{\cdot}4630 \times \log 2800\ ;$$

$$S_a = 3{\cdot}5062\ .$$

5. The temperature of the combustion products in the exhaust section of the nozzle T_{exh} is determined according to formula (3.13).

$p_{c.c}$	20	40	60	80	100
$T_{c.c}$ °K	1932	1707	1599	1517	1452

An example of the calculation for $p_{c \cdot c} = 20$ atm is :

$$\log T_{exh} = \frac{3 \cdot 5062}{2 \cdot 303 \times 0 \cdot 4630} = 3 \cdot 286 ;$$

$$T_{exh} = 1932 °K.$$

6. We determine i_{exh} according to equation (2.51).

$p_{c.c}$	20	40	60	80	100
i_{exh}	1222·1	1115·7	1065·7	1027·7	997·7

An example of the calculation for $p_{c \cdot c} = 20$ atm is :

$$i_{exh} = 1621 \cdot 7 + 0 \cdot 4630\,(1932 - 2800) + 0 ;$$

$$i_{exh} = 1222 \cdot 1 .$$

7. We determine P_{sp} .

$p_{c.c}$	20	40	60	80	100
P_{sp}	222·9	242·8	251·7	258·1	263·0

An example of the calculation for $p_{c \cdot c} = 20$ atm is :

$$P_{sp} = 9 \cdot 33 \sqrt{(1791 \cdot 9 - 1222 \cdot 1)} ;$$

$$P_{sp} = 222 \cdot 9 \text{ kg} \cdot \text{sec/kg}.$$

The results of the calculation are shown in the graph in Fig. 8.

EXAMPLE 5. To establish the dependence of the specific thrust and temperature of the combustion products in the exhaust section of the nozzle of a liquid rocket engine, operating on 95 per cent by weight ethyl alcohol (admixture — water) and liquid oxygen, on the pressure of the combustion products in the exhaust section of the nozzle p_{exh} for variations of p_{exh} within the range 0·2–1·0 atm.

The excess oxidant coefficient is $\alpha_0' = 0 \cdot 7$ ($\alpha' = 0 \cdot 748$), the pressure of the combustion products in the combustion chamber of the engine $p_{c \cdot c} = 50$ atm.

It can be seen from the conditions, that the composition of the fuel components, the excess oxidant coefficient and the pressure of the combustion products in the combustion chamber are the same in the given example as in Example 2 of this section. The solution of the problem (up to the determination of the entropy of the combustion products in the combustion chamber $S_{c \cdot c}$) is handled as shown in Example 2. We shall carry out the calculation further according to the

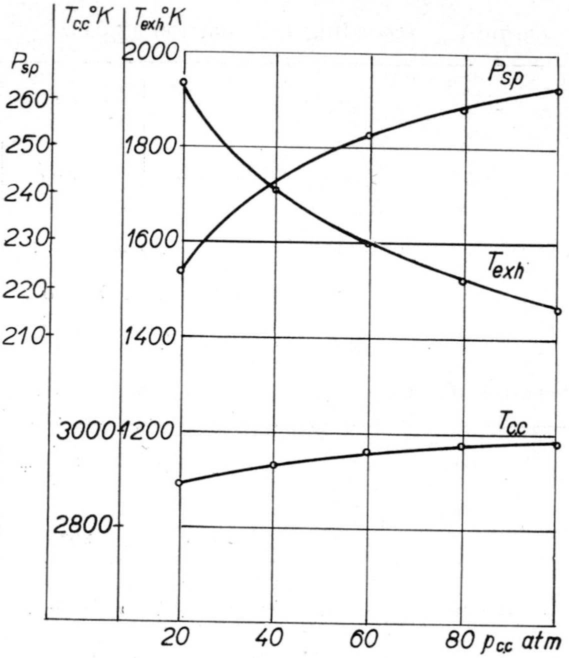

FIG. 8

scheme described in Section 14B. We assign values for $p_{exh} = 1{\cdot}0$; $0{\cdot}8$; $0{\cdot}5$; $0{\cdot}2$ atm, and continue the calculation for the chosen values of p_{exh}.

1. We find S_a according to formula (3.11).

p_{exh}	1·0	0·8	0·5	0·2
S_a	3·8525	3·8368	3·7935	3·7143

An example of the calculation for $p_{exh} = 0{\cdot}8$ atm is :

$$S_a = -\,0{\cdot}2295 + 2{\cdot}303 \times 0{\cdot}5142 \times \log 2800 +$$
$$+\, 2{\cdot}303 \times 0{\cdot}001986 \log 0{\cdot}8\,;$$
$$S_a = 3{\cdot}8525.$$

2. Since in all cases here $S_a/c^0_{p,L} < 7{\cdot}50$, then the calculation of T_{exh} is carried out according to formula (3.13).

p_{exh}	1·0	0·8	0·5	0·2
T_{exh} °K .	1780	1734	1585	1356

An example of the calculation for $p_{\text{exh}} = 0{\cdot}8$ atm is :

$$\log T_{\text{exh}} = \frac{3{\cdot}8368}{2{\cdot}303 \times 0{\cdot}5142} = 3{\cdot}239\,;$$

$$T_{\text{exh}} = 1734 \ \ {}^\circ\text{K}\,.$$

3. The enthalpy of the combustion products in the exhaust section of the nozzle i_{exh} is determined from equation (2.51).

p_{exh}	1·0	0·8	0·5	0·2
i_{exh}	1707·0	1683·8	1607·2	1489·2

An example of the calculation for $p_{\text{exh}} = 0{\cdot}8$ atm is :

$$i_{\text{exh}} = 2232 + 0{\cdot}5142\,(1734 - 2800) + 0\,;$$

$$i_{\text{exh}} = 1683{\cdot}8 \ \ \text{kcal/kg}.$$

4. We determine P_{sp} .

p_{exh}	1·0	0·8	0·5	0·2
P_{sp}	272·5	276·0	288·0	305·2

An example of the calculation for $P_{\text{exh}} = 0{\cdot}8$ atm is :

$$P_{\text{sp}} = 9{\cdot}33 \sqrt{(2559 - 1683{\cdot}8)}\,;$$

$$P_{\text{sp}} = 276{\cdot}0 \ \ \text{kg}\cdot\text{sec/kg}.$$

An entropy diagram has been constructed for the given case by G. B. Sinyarev and M.V. Dobrovol'skii.[(9)] The results of our calculations can be compared with the data from the diagram.

p_{exh} atm	T_{exh}, °K		P_{sp}, $\frac{kg \cdot sec}{kg}$		Error in specific thrust, %
	By calculation	From the diagram	By calculation	From the diagram	
1·0	1780	1780	272·5	273·7	0·4
0·8	1734	No data	276·0	No data	—
0·5	1585	1565	288·0	289·0	0·3
0·2	1356	1340	305·2	306·0	0·3

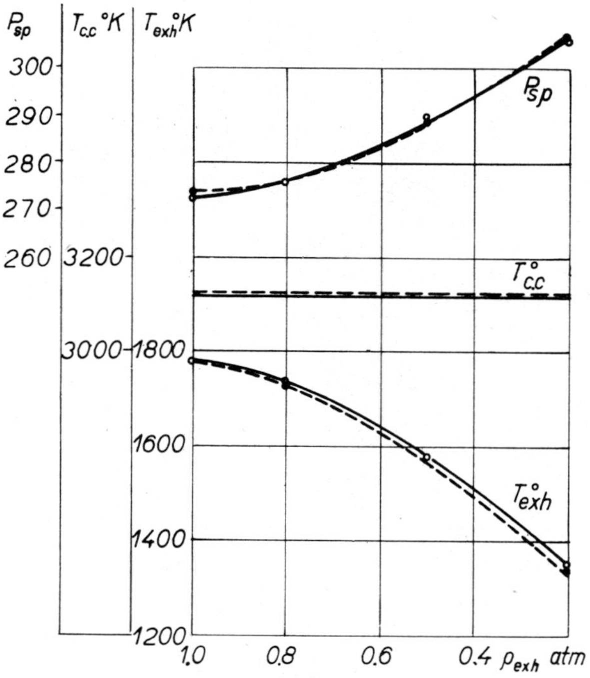

FIG. 9

Figure 9 shows a graph, constructed according to the results of the calculations we have carried out. The broken lines on the graph refer to data from the entropy diagram.

16. Accuracy of the Calculations

Let us consider the accuracy of the calculations according to the proposed method. We shall assume that the methods of thermodynamical assessment of rocket engines, based on preliminary determination of the composition of the combustion products, are accurate. The degree of accuracy of calculation of the primary operating characteristics of an engine by approximate methods can be assessed if we compare the values of these characteristics as determined by the precise method, and by the approximate method proposed in the present book.

It was mentioned earlier that the enthalpy of the undissociated combustion products i^0, is calculated with an error not exceeding 0·4 per cent of its value by the approximate expressions established in the present book, and in the absolute majority of cases considered the error does not exceed 0·1–0·2 per cent. The enthalpy i^0 comprises the main fraction of the enthalpy of the dissociated combustion products. The parameter Δi — the increase in enthalpy of the combustion products as a result of dissociation — in all cases plays a correction role to the parameter i^0, which is greater the higher the temperature and the lower the pressure.

In the present work, such a system is adopted for the construction of curves, which eliminates obtaining a large error in the calculation of Δi, namely:

— for a temperature of the combustion products less than 1800–1900°K, the magnitude of the parameter Δi can be neglected in view of its smallness;

— for a temperature of the combustion products found within the approximate limits of 1900–2400°K, Δi is small with respect to the absolute value and therefore the possible error in its determination has practically no influence on the results of the calculation;

— for a temperature of the combustion products in the exhaust section of the engine nozzle which is higher, approaching 2600–2800 °K, the possible error in determining Δi becomes a minimum, since the curves for determining the parameter $\Delta i_{L\ v\ \Phi}$ in the given temperature region L are constructed for a temperature of 2800°K;

— for a temperature of the combustion products in the combustion chamber of the engine of 3200–3600 °K, the error in determining Δi will be a minimum, since the curves for the parameter $\Delta i_{H,v,\Phi}$ are constructed in the temperature region H at a temperature of 3400°K.

It was pointed out earlier that the interpolation formulae of the form (2.35) are approximate, and the method of calculation of the power index n_{eff} recommended in the present book is not precise (see Chapter 2, Section 7).

For this reason the accuracy of calculation of the operating characteristics of an engine increases, if the thermodynamical calculation of the engine is carried out for a pressure of the combustion products in the combustion chamber $p_{c \cdot c} = 40$ atm and in the exhaust section of the nozzle $p_{exh} = 1$ atm. Since the nomograms for determining the parameters $\Delta i_{H, v, \Phi}$ and $\Delta i_{L, v, \Phi}$ are constructed precisely for these values of pressure, then this circumstance eliminates the carrying out of interpolation with respect to pressure and enables the errors associated with it to be avoided.

The degree of accuracy of calculation of the operating characteristics of an engine, as the calculations carried out by us have shown, remains completely satisfactory if the calculation be carried out for a pressure of the combustion products in the combustion chamber exceeding 20 atm.

In speaking of the accuracy of the calculations according to the proposed method, it is necessary to emphasize the fact that all calculations, on the basis of which the approximate mathematical expressions are established and the nomograms are constructed, were carried out by the usual methods, taking into account six dissociation reactions and the oxidation reaction of nitrogen in the combustion products. According to the considerations presented above, it is impossible to anticipate large-scale errors also in the final results of the calculations. The sufficiently large number of thermodynamical calculations carried out by the proposed method permits confirmation that the maximum error in the determination of specific thrust in calculating it by the proposed method does not exceed 1 per cent of its value in the absolute majority of cases. The error in determining the temperature of the combustion products is not greater than 40–50°.

Such an error in technical calculations is quite permissible, all the more since the law of variation of the operating characteristics of an engine from the most important parameters (X_C, X_H, α, $p_{c \cdot c}$, p_{exh}) is completely maintained.

CHAPTER 4

Calculation of the chemical composition of the combustion products at high temperatures

IN carrying out thermodynamical assessment of rocket engines by the method recommended in the present book, it is not necessary, as was shown earlier, to carry out a preliminary calculation of the chemical composition of the combustion products. However, in certain special cases, in particular for calculation of a coolant system, and also for carrying out particularly accurate calculations of the operating characteristics of an engine, the need arises for calculating the chemical composition of the combustion products.

In the present chapter, the method of calculation of the composition of the combustion products is given, taking into account their dissociation. The method permits the composition of the combustion products of a fuel to be computed within a range of pressures approximately from 0·5 to 100 atm, and at temperatures up to 3600°K. The labour-consuming nature of the calculations by the proposed method is several times less than as a result of calculating the combustion products by the well-known methods of successive approximations.

The essence of the proposed method of calculation consists in the following: the system of equations of equilibrium and material balance (2.19) is reduced to a quadratic equation of relative magnitude $n = p_{H_2O}/p_{H_2}$, which is solved by the method of successive approximations together with the use of the families of curves (Figs. 21–42 of the Appendix.) In deriving the computing equation, no simplifications or substitutions of the existing relationships have been carried out; the reduction in the accuracy of determination of the content of the individual components of the combustion products occurs only as a consequence of the errors in working with the nomograms referred to.

The special feature of the proposed method is the fact that for the calculation is assigned not the actual pressure of the combustion products p, but the arbitrary pressure of the undissociated products p^0.

The quantities p^0 and p are related to each other in the following manner :

$$p = p^0 + \Delta p,$$

where Δp is the change in pressure of the combustion products as a result of dissociation at constant volume.

17. Derivation of the Computing Equation

In order to derive the computing equation we shall carry out a number of transformations of the existing equations; we compile an algebraic sum of the form

$$A_1' = X_C + X_H - p. \tag{4.1}$$

Taking into account equations (2.6) and (2.7) we obtain

$$A_1' = p_{H_2O} + p_{H_2} - p_{O_2} - p_O - p_{NO} - p_{N_2} - p_N. \tag{4.2}$$

Expression (4.2), taking into account (2.8), can be written in the form

$$A_1' = p_{H_2O} + p_{H_2} - p_{O_2} - p_O - 0{\cdot}5p_{NO} - 0{\cdot}5p_N - 0{\cdot}5X_N.$$

Denoting

$$A_4' = A_1' + 0{\cdot}5X_N, \tag{4.3}$$

we obtain

$$A_4' = p_{H_2O} + p_{H_2} - p_{O_2} - p_O - 0{\cdot}5p_{NO} - 0{\cdot}5p_N. \tag{4.4}$$

We now compile an algebraic sum of the form

$$A_2' = X_C + X_O + X_H + X_N - 2p. \tag{4.5}$$

By consideration of equations (2.5)–(2.8) we obtain

$$A_2' = p_{CO_2} + p_{H_2O} - p_H - p_O - p_N. \tag{4.6}$$

And, finally, we compile the algebraic sum

$$A_3' = X_C - X_O - X_N + p. \tag{4.7}$$

Substituting the values of the component right-hand sides in accordance with equations (2.5), (2.6), and (2.8), we can write

$$A_3' = p_{CO} + p_{H_2} + p_H + p_{O_2} - p_{NO} - p_{N_2}. \tag{4.8}$$

We shall introduce one further parameter into our considerations

$$A_5' = A_3' + 0{\cdot}5X_N. \tag{4.9}$$

It is not difficult to show that

$$A_5' = p_{CO} + p_{H_2} + p_H - p_{O_2} + 0{\cdot}5p_N - 0{\cdot}5p_{NO}. \qquad (4.10)$$

From expression (4.2) we find the relationship between p_{H_2} and p_O:

$$p_{H_2O} + p_{H_2} - p_O = A_1' + E\,, \qquad (4.11)$$

where

$$E = p_{O_2} + p_{NO} + p_{N_2} + p_N = p_{O_2} + 0{\cdot}5p_{NO} + 0{\cdot}5p_N + 0{\cdot}5X_N. \qquad (4.11a)$$

Further derivations are simplified if equilibrium constants are introduced into the derivatives being considered, related to the primary derivatives in the following manner:

$$K_8 = K_4\sqrt{K_2} = \frac{p_H\sqrt[4]{p_{O_2}}}{\sqrt{p_{H_2O}}}; \quad K_9 = K_5K_2 = \frac{p_Op_{H_2}}{p_{H_2O}};$$

$$K_{10} = K_7K_2 = \frac{p_{NO}p_{H_2}}{p_{H_2O}\sqrt{p_{N_2}}}; \quad K_{11} = \frac{K_3}{\sqrt{K_2}} = \frac{p_{OH}}{\sqrt{p_{H_2O}}\sqrt[4]{p_{O_2}}};$$

$$K_{12} = K_2^2 = \frac{p_{O_2}p_{H_2}^2}{p_{H_2O}^2}.$$

Substituting in (4.11) the value of the parameter p_{H_2O}, expressed via the equilibrium constant K_9, we find

$$p_{H_2} = \frac{A_1' + E + p_O}{n+1}, \qquad (4.12)$$

where

$$n = \frac{p_{H_2O}}{p_{H_2}} = \frac{p_O}{K_9}.$$

It follows from (4.8) that

$$p_{CO} = A_3' + E - p_{H_2} - p_H - p_N. \qquad (4.13)$$

Substituting in (4.13) the value of p_{H_2} from (4.12), we obtain

$$\frac{X_C}{1+Kn} = \frac{A_3'n + A_3' - A_1' + En - p_O - (p_H + p_N)(1+n)}{1+n}. \qquad (4.14)$$

We shall investigate what the right-hand side of equation (4.14) represents. The numerical values of the parameters A_1', A_2' and A_3' cannot be determined prior to calculation of the chemical composition of the combustion products, since the quantity p — the pressure of the dissociated products — is unknown.

However, there is the overall possibility of calculating the values of the parameters A_1, A_2 and A_3, by the determinate expressions

$$A_1 = X_C + X_H - p^0 ; \tag{4.15}$$

$$A_2 = X_C + X_H + X_O + X_N - 2p^0 ; \tag{4.16}$$

$$A_3 = X_C + X_O - X_N + p^0, \tag{4.17}$$

since according to (2.18)

$$X_C = X_C^0 ; \quad X_H = X_H^0 ; \quad X_O = X_O^0 ; \quad X_N = X_N^0 .$$

We shall assume that the pressure of the undissociated combustion products p^0, as mentioned above, is unknown. Taking into account that

$$p^0 = p - \Delta p,$$

by simultaneous consideration of expressions (4.1), (4.5), (4.7), (4.15), (4.16), and (4.17) we obtain

$$A_1' = A_1 - \Delta p ; \tag{4.18}$$

$$A_2' = A_2 - 2\,\Delta p ; \tag{4.19}$$

$$A_3' = A_3 + \Delta p ; \tag{4.20}$$

and further

$$A_4' = A_1 - \Delta p + 0{\cdot}5\, X_N = A_4 - \Delta p , \tag{4.21}$$

$$A_5' = A_3 + \Delta\, p + 0{\cdot}5\, X_N = A_5 + \Delta p . \tag{4.22}$$

By taking into account the expressions obtained, we transform (4.14) :

$$\frac{X_C}{1 + Kn} = \frac{A_3 n + A_3 - A_1 + n\Delta p + 2\Delta p + En - P_O - (p_H + p_N)(1 + n)}{1 + n} . \tag{4.23}$$

Obviously, the numerical value of the parameter Δp is equal to the total pressure of the dissociation products (for $a < 1$, these are O_2, OH, NO, O, H, N) after deduction of the diminution of pressure of the "primary" gases present in the undissociated combustion products. The total pressure of the dissociated products is

$$p_{diss} = p_{O_2} + p_{OH} + p_{NO} + p_O + p_H + p_N .$$

The reduction in the partial pressure of the "primary" combustion products as a result of dissociation can be found from a comparison of expressions (1.11)–(1.14) and (2.5)–(2.8). Thus, for balance with respect to the chemical element — hydrogen — the following expressions hold good:

$$X_H^0 = 2p_{H_2O}^0 + 2p_{H_2}^0;$$

$$X_H = 2p_{H_2O} + 2p_{H_2} + p_{OH} + p_H.$$

In accordance with (2.18)

$$X_H = X_H^0.$$

Denoting

$$\Delta p_{H_2O} = p_{H_2O}^0 - p_{H_2O};$$

$$\Delta p_{H_2} = p_{H_2}^0 - p_{H_2},$$

we obtain that the total reduction of the partial pressures of water vapour and diatomic hydrogen as a result of dissociation is equal to:

$$\Delta p_{H_2O} + \Delta p_{H_2} = 0{\cdot}5p_{OH} + 0{\cdot}5p_H.$$

Similarly for the other chemical elements we obtain

$$\Delta p_{CO_2} + \Delta p_{CO} = 0;$$

$$\Delta p_{N_2} = 0{\cdot}5p_{NO} + 0{\cdot}5p_N.$$

Then by definition

$$\Delta p = p_{diss} - (\Delta p_{H_2O} + \Delta p_{H_2} + \Delta p_{CO_2} + \Delta p_{CO} + \Delta p_{N_2})$$

or finally

$$\Delta p = 0{\cdot}5\,(p_H + p_{OH} + p_N + p_{NO}) + p_{O_2} + p_O. \tag{4.23a}$$

Taking into account formulae (4.23a) and (4.11a) we obtain

$$\frac{X_C}{1+Kn} = \frac{A_5 n + A_3 - A_1 + \left(0{\cdot}5p_{OH} + \frac{1}{n}\,p_{OH} - 0{\cdot}5p_H\right) n + (1+n)\,(p_{NO} + p_O + 2p_{O_2})}{1+n} \tag{4.24}$$

Here

$$A_5 = 2X_C - X_O + 0{\cdot}5X_H, \tag{4.25}$$

$$A_3 - A_1 = 2X_C - X_O. \tag{4.26}$$

From comparison of (4.25) with (4.26) it follows also that

$$A_3 - A_1 = A_5 - 0{\cdot}5X_H. \tag{4.27}$$

We denote

$$B_1 = 0{\cdot}5p_{OH} + \frac{1}{n}p_{OH} - 0{\cdot}5p_H\,, \tag{4.28}$$

$$B_2 = p_{NO} + p_O + 2p_{O_2}\,. \tag{4.29}$$

Equation (4.24), taking into account (4.25)–(4.29) assumes the form

$$\frac{X_C}{1+Kn} = \frac{A_5n + A_5 - 0{\cdot}5X_H + B_1n + B_2(n+1)}{1+n}. \tag{4.30}$$

We transform the expression for B_1:

$$B_1 = 0{\cdot}5p_{OH} + \frac{1}{n}p_{OH} - 0{\cdot}5p_H = 0{\cdot}5K_3\frac{p_{OH}}{\sqrt{p_{H_2}}} + \frac{1}{n}K_3\frac{p_{H_2O}}{\sqrt{p_{H_2}}} -$$

$$- 0{\cdot}5K_4\sqrt{p_{H_2}} = \sqrt{p_{H_2}}\,[(0{\cdot}5n+1)\,K_3 - 0{\cdot}5K_4]. \tag{4.31}$$

We express $\sqrt{p_{H_2}}$ via the relationship $n = p_{H_2O}/p_{H_2}$.

For p_{H_2} we have obtained the expression

$$p_{H_2} = \frac{A_1' + E + p_O}{1+n} = \frac{A_1 - \Delta p + E + p_O}{1+n}. \tag{4.12}$$

Considering simultaneously (4.12), (4.23a) and (4.11a), we find

$$p_{H_2} = \frac{A_4 - 0{\cdot}5\,(p_{OH} + p_H)}{1+n}\,,$$

or

$$p_{H_2} = \frac{A_4 - 0{\cdot}5\,\sqrt{p_{H_2}}\,(K_3n + K_4)}{n+1}\,,$$

since

$$p_{OH} = K_3\frac{p_{H_2O}}{\sqrt{p_{H_2}}} \quad\text{and}\quad p_H = K_4\sqrt{p_{H_2}}\,,$$

and further

$$\sqrt{p_{H_2}} = \frac{-b' + \sqrt{(b'^2 - 4a'c')}}{2a'}\,, \tag{4.32}$$

where

$$b' = 0{\cdot}5(K_3\,n + K_4)\,;$$

$$a' = n + 1\,;$$

$$c' = -A_4\,.$$

Thus, the parameter B_1 turns out to be a function of the temperature, of the elementary chemical composition of the fuel and of the ratio $n = p_{H_2O}/p_{H_2}$.

Let us now consider the parameter B_2 :

$$B_2 = p_{NO} + p_O + 2p_{O_2} .$$

It is known that

$$p_{NO} = K_{10}\, n \sqrt{p_{N_2}} ;$$

$$p_O = K_9\, n ;$$

$$p_{O_2} = K_{12}\, n^2 .$$

We determine p_{N_2} under dissociation conditions :

$$p_{N_2} = 0{\cdot}5X_N - 0{\cdot}5K_{10}n \sqrt{(p_{N_2})} - 0{\cdot}5K_6 \sqrt{p_{N_2}} .$$

The quantity p_{N_2} can be found from this equation by solving it relative to $\sqrt{p_{N_2}}$. However, in practically all cases the calculation can be simplified by substituting in the right-hand side of the equation

$$\sqrt{p_{N_2}} \approx 0{\cdot}5X_N .$$

Thus,

$$p_{N_2} \approx 0{\cdot}5X_N - 0{\cdot}5(K_{10}\, n + K_6) \sqrt{0{\cdot}5X_N} .$$

Finally, for B_2 we obtain

$$B_2 = [(K_{10} \sqrt{(p_{N_2})} + K_9 + K_{12}\, n]\, n . \tag{4.33}$$

We transcribe equation (4.30) in the following form :

$$\frac{X_C}{1 + Kn} = \frac{(A_5 + B_1 + B_2)n + A_5 - 0{\cdot}5X_H + B_2}{1 + n} .$$

Solving (4.30) relative to n, we obtain a quadratic equation of the form :

$$an^2 + bn + c = 0 , \tag{4.34}$$

where

$$\left.\begin{aligned} a &= K(A_5 + B_1 + B_2) ; \\ b &= (A_5 + B_1 + B_2) + K(A_5 - 0{\cdot}5X_H + B_2) - X_C ; \\ c &= (A_5 - 0{\cdot}5X_H + B_2) - X_C . \end{aligned}\right\} \tag{4.35}$$

If it be assumed that $B_1 = B_2 = 0$, then equation (4.34) is transformed into the usual quadratic equation relative to $n_0 = p^0_{H_2O}/p_{H_2}$ for the undissociated combustion products at the same temperature.

In the case of the dissociated combustion products, the parameters B_1 and B_2 are not equal to zero. It can be seen from (4.31) that the parameter B_1 depends on the temperature, the ratios n and A_4. Since

$$A_4 = A_1 + 0{\cdot}5X_N = X_C + X_H - p^0 + 0{\cdot}5X_N = X_C + X_H - X_C - \\ - 0{\cdot}5X_H - 0{\cdot}5X_N + 0{\cdot}5X_N = 0{\cdot}5X_H ,$$

then in the final reckoning B_1 will depend on the temperature, n and X_H. The parameter B_2 depends on the temperature, n and X_N.

18. Methods of Calculating the Chemical Composition of the Combustion Products

We shall assume that it is required to take into consideration the chemical composition of the dissociated combustion products for a given elementary chemical composition of the fuel and temperature T. By using the method of calculation proposed we shall discuss the mode of solution of this problem.

It is known that calculation of the partial pressures of the individual components of the combustion products is carried out extremely simply, if the partial pressure of one of the components is known, or the ratio of any two components, for example $n = p_{H_2O}/p_{H_2}$.

In calculations by the proposed method, the most important aim is to find the quantity n. Calculation of the parameter n is carried out by the method of successive approximation according to the method explained below. Having assigned a certain value for n_1 (first approximation), we determine the parameters B_1 and B_2 and, solving equation (4.34), we find the value n_2. The true value of n will be found between n_1 and n_2, whereupon, as the practice of calculations shows, the value of n is located close to n_2. For this reason, it is expedient to assign a value for n_3 as a second approximation, determined by the formula

$$n_3 = \frac{2}{3} n_2 + \frac{1}{3} n_1 . \qquad (4.36)$$

The parameters B_1 and B_2 are again determined for the value n_3 and as a result of solving equation (4.34) the value of n_4 is found which is then compared with n_3.

The calculation is continued until the values of the parameter n, selected for the calculation, coincide with the value of this parameter obtained by equation (4.34), or until close values are obtained. Usually, the problem is solved in two or three attempts. The value found for n is then used to determine the partial pressures of the components of the combustion products.

What value of n is assigned initially?

For an approximate determination of n_1 one should obtain $B_1 = B_2 = 0$ and according to equation (4.34) one should determine n_0 — the ratio of the partial pressures of the same gases in the absence of dissociation. It is well-known, that as a result of dissociation the partial pressure of water vapour is reduced, but the partial pressure of diatomic hydrogen increases. Thus, in all cases $n < n_0$. In order to reduce the number of trials, the initial value of n_1 should be taken as somewhat less than n_0.

As yet, nothing has been said as to the manner in which the quantities B_1 and B_2 should be calculated. It is undesirable to determine them by equations (4.31) and (4.33). The operation mentioned can be avoided by calculating beforehand B_1 and B_2 for a series of temperatures and constructing the corresponding graphs. For B_1 and B_2, nomograms of two forms are constructed :

— for a region of quite high pressures and temperatures :

$$p = 3\text{–}100 \text{ atm}, \quad T = 2600\text{–}3600\,^\circ\text{K};$$

(see Figs. 21–32 of the Appendix)

— for a region of relatively low pressures and temperatures:

$$p = 0{\cdot}5\text{–}3 \text{ atm}, \quad T = 2000\text{–}2800\,^\circ\text{K}$$

(see Figs. 33–42 of the Appendix).

The families of curves in Figs. 21–32 of the Appendix are intended primarily for determining the chemical composition of the dissociated combustion products in the combustion chamber of a liquid rocket engine. The families of curves in Figs. 33–42 of the Appendix permit the chemical composition of the combustion products in the exhaust section of the nozzle to be determined. The quite wide range of variation of the quantity n makes it possible to use these nomograms for practically all cases of interest to us of the excess oxygen coefficient a.

Having determined the ratio $n = p_{H_2O}/p_{H_2}$, it is easy to calculate the chemical composition of the combustion products according to the well-known relationships

$$b' = 0{\cdot}5(K_3 n + K_4)\,;$$

$$a' = n + 1\,;\quad c' = -\,0{\cdot}5X_H\,;$$

$$\sqrt{p_{H_2}} = \frac{-\,b' + \sqrt{(b'^2 - 4a'c')}}{2a'}\,;$$

$$p_{H_2O} = n p_{H_2}\,;\; p_{OH} = \frac{p_{H_2O}}{\sqrt{p_{H_2}}} K_3\,;$$

$$p_H = K_4\sqrt{p_{H_2}}\,;\quad p_O = K_9 n\,;\quad \sqrt{p_{O_2}} = K_2 n\,;$$

$$p_{CO} = \frac{X_C}{1 + Kn}\,;\quad p_{CO_2} = X_C - p_{CO}\,;$$

$$\sqrt{p_{N_2}} = -\,0{\cdot}25K_{10}n + \sqrt{[(0{\cdot}25K_{10}n)^2 + 0{\cdot}5X_N]}\,;$$

$$p_{NO} = K_{10}n\sqrt{p_{N_2}}\,;\quad p_N = K_6\sqrt{p_{N_2}}\,;$$

$$p_{N_2} = 0{\cdot}5X_N - 0{\cdot}5(p_{NO} + p_N).$$

As a result of the necessity for the repeated carrying out of any special calculation within the range of variation of the parameters n, X_H, X_N and T, not embraced by the nomograms constructed, the latter can be easily constructed according to the well-known relationships of (4.31) and (4.33). In those cases the number of special calculations carried out is small and the addition of the nomograms is devoid of meaning, the calculations can be carried out without the nomograms, using equations (4.31) and (4.33) for determining the parameters B_1 and B_2.

The principle of calculating the chemical composition of the combustion products, as suggested in this book, holds good for all values whatsoever of the equilibrium constants. However, the families of curves are constructed for actual values of the equilibrium constants presented in Table 2 of the Appendix. Since the equilibrium constants are being defined more precisely with the course of time, then as a result of the necessity for determining B_1 and B_2 for new values of the constants, new families of curves may be constructed or equations (4.31) and (4.33) may even be used directly.

In order to calculate the enthalpy and entropy of the combustion products, tabulated values can be used of the enthalpy and entropy of the individual gases — the dissociation products — independently of what system of principles of reading these parameters is adopted for determining their numerical values. In particular, Tables 1 and 3 of the Appendix can be used.

The calculation of the chemical composition of the combustion products is carried out more simply for those values of temperature for which the families of curves in Figs. 21–42 of the Appendix are constructed. The chemical composition for intermediate values of temperature are best determined by a graphical interpolation method with respect to the known partial pressures of the components of the combustion products at three or four neighbouring temperatures. If so desired, the calculation of the chemical composition of the combustion products may be carried out for any chosen temperature. For this it is necessary to have previously constructed graphs of the dependence of the equilibrium constants on the temperature and to determine the parameters B_1 and B_2 not by a nomogram but directly according to equations (4.31) and (4.33).

In order to calculate the composition of the combustion products and in the first instance in order to determine the values of the resulting parameters X_C, X_H, X_N and X_0 according to formulae (1.10), (1.15)–(1.17) and (2.18), it is necessary to assign a value for p^0 — the pressure of the combustion products in the absence of dissociation. The actual pressure of the dissociated combustion products p, the composition of which is determined by the calculation, exceeds p^0 by a quantity Δp.

Since the quantity Δp depends on the temperature of the combustion products, then it is obvious that for an invariable value of p^0 the pressure of the dissociated combustion products p will have different values at different temperatures.

In order to assess rocket engines, this method of calculating the combustion products is convenient, since the composition of the combustion products in rocket engines is determined for a specified pressure p.

In this case the quantity Δp should be previously calculated, and then the quantity p^0 corresponding to the pressure p.

In temperature region H (above 2800°K), in order to calculate the parameter Δp for specified pressure and temperature of the dissociated combustion products, the equation can be used

$$\Delta p = \frac{p}{130 \times 40} \Delta i_{H, v, \Phi} \left(\frac{p_{H,\Phi}}{p}\right)^{n_{\text{eff}}} \left(\frac{T - 2200}{T_{H\,\Phi} - 2200}\right)^{m_H}. \qquad (4.37)$$

Equation (4.37) is obtained as a result of simultaneous consideration of equations (2.43) and (2.34) taking into account the circumstance that in the general case p is not equal to 40 atm . The parameters $\Delta i_{H,v,\Phi}$, n_{eff} and m_H are determined, as previously, according to curves and formulae of Chapter 2 of the present book, for the value of a for which the calculation of the composition of the combustion products is carried out (the value of m_H does not depend on a). The numerical values of the parameters $X_C = X_C^0$ and $X_H = X_H^0$, with the aid of which are determined the values of $\Delta i_{H,v,\Phi}$, n_{eff} and m_H according to the curves and formulae of Chapter 2, are found by formulae (1.39) and (1.40) for a given fuel independently of the temperature T and pressure p of the dissociated combustion products assumed for the calculation.

The parameter Δp depends on the temperature and pressure of the dissociated combustion products and varies with change of pressure and temperature in accordance with equation (4.37). If the magnitude of the pressure p remains invariable, and only the temperature is varied, then Δp will vary in accordance with the change of temperature. Simultaneously, with a change of Δp the unknown pressure of the undissociated combustion products will also vary (we shall call this p_T^0), since

$$p_T^0 = p - \Delta p . \qquad (4.38)$$

In order that the pressure of the undissociated combustion products should be equal to the chosen pressure p, it is necessary that the parameters X_C and X_H, used in the nomograms of Figs. 21–42 of the Appendix for determining B_1 and B_2, should be calculated according to the formulae

$$X_{C_T} = p_T^0 \, \mu^0 \, A_C ; \qquad (4.39)$$

$$X_{H_T} = p_T^0 \, \mu^0 \, A_H . \qquad (4.40)$$

The values of the parameters X_{C_T} and X_{H_T} can be used for determining the parameters B_1 and B_2 according to the curves, only for that value of temperature at which the calculation is carried out of the chemical composition of the combustion products. In the case of the calculations being carried out for another temperature of the combustion products, it is necessary to determine a new value for Δp according to equation (4.37) and with it to find the new values of p_T^0, X_{C_T}, X_{H_T}.

Practice shows, however, that for a number of reasons the pressure of the dissociated combustion products is not always obtained precisely equal to the specified pressure p, but differs somewhat from it to one side or other. In the case when the difference is small, the partial pressures of all the components of the combustion products may be correspondingly decreased or increased, by assuming a linear law for the variation of the partial pressures from the overall pressure. For a more or less significant difference the calculation should be repeated for revised values of X_{C_T} X_{H_T} (multiplied by the ratio of the specified pressure of the dissociated combustion products to that obtained).

For temperatures lying within temperature region L (below 2800-°K), in order to determinate the parameter Δp at a pressure p, the equat ion is used

$$\Delta p = \frac{p}{130} i_{L,v,\Phi} \left(\frac{1}{p}\right)^{n_{\text{eff}}} \left(\frac{T - 1400}{T_{L,\Phi} - 1400}\right)^{m_L}. \tag{4.41}$$

19. Examples of the Calculation of the Chemical Composition of the Dissociated Combustion Products

Four examples of the calculation of chemical composition are carried out below according to the proposed method. The first two of them are related to a fuel consisting primarily of hydrogen and not containing nitrogen. The two succeeding examples of the calculation refer to a fuel consisting primarily of carbon and nitrogen.

The sequences of the calculation of the chemical composition of the combustion products are shown in Examples 1 and 3, for a specified pressure p^0.

In Examples 2 and 4 the calculation is carried out of the chemical composition of the combustion products at a specified pressure p of the dissociated combustion products.

EXAMPLE 1. To calculate the composition of the combustion products of a fuel characterized by the parameters $X_C = 14$, $X_H = 52$, $X_N = 0$, $a = 0{\cdot}8945$ for $p^0 = 40$ atm and $T = 3000$°K.

1. We determine the ratio $n_0 = p^0_{H_2O}/p^0_{H_2}$ (in the absence of dissociation). With this objective we carry out the following successive calculations :

(a) we find the independent parameter for oxygen :

$$X_O = (2X_C + 0{\cdot}5X_H) ;$$

$$X_O = (2 \times 14 + 0{\cdot}5 \times 52)\, 0{\cdot}8945 ;$$

$$X_O = 48{\cdot}34;$$

(b) we determine the coefficient A_5 :

$$A_5 = 2X_C - X_O + 0{\cdot}5X_H ;$$
$$A_5 = 2 \times 14 - 48{\cdot}34 + 0{\cdot}5 \times 52 ;$$
$$A_5 = 5{\cdot}66 ;$$

(c) we establish, by equation (4.35) the value of the coefficients of the quadratic equation, assuming

$$B_1 = B_2 = 0 ;$$
$$a = K \times A_5 ;$$
$$a = 0{\cdot}1445 \times 5{\cdot}66 ;$$
$$a = 0{\cdot}8182 ;$$
$$b = 5{\cdot}66 + 0{\cdot}1445\,(5{\cdot}66 - 0{\cdot}5 + 52) - 14 ;$$
$$b = -11{\cdot}282 ;$$
$$c = (A_5 - 0{\cdot}5X_H) - X_C ;$$
$$c = (5{\cdot}66 - 26) - 14 ;$$
$$c = -34{\cdot}34 ;$$

(d) we find n_0

$$n_0 = \frac{11{\cdot}282 + \sqrt{(11{\cdot}282^2 + 4 \times 0{\cdot}8182 \times 34{\cdot}34)}}{2 \times 0{\cdot}8182} ;$$

$$n_0 = 16{\cdot}35.$$

2. The ratio n is determined for the specified conditions.

(a) As a first approximation we choose

$$n_1 < n_0 = 14 .$$

From the nomogram in Fig. 27 of the Appendix we find $B_1 = 0{\cdot}925$.

From the nomogram in Fig. 28 of the Appendix we find $B_2 = 1{\cdot}02$.

We determine the coefficients of the quadratic equation (4.34) according to formula (4.35) :

$$a = 1{\cdot}099 ; \quad b = -9{\cdot}183 ; \quad c = -33{\cdot}32.$$

Solving equation (4.34) we find

$$n_2 = 11{\cdot}09 .$$

The difference in the values of n_1 and n_2 as obtained is quite considerable.

(b) As a second approximation we choose n_3, found according to formula (4.36) :

$$n_3 = \frac{2}{3} \times 11{\cdot}09 + \frac{1}{3} \times 14 = 12{\cdot}07 .$$

After rounding off, $n_3 = 12$.

From the curves in Fig. 27 of the Appendix we find $B_1 = 0{\cdot}858$.
From the curves in Fig. 28 of the Appendix we find $B_2 = 0{\cdot}76$.
We find the coefficients of equation (4.34):

$$a = 1{\cdot}051\ ;\quad b = -9{\cdot}552\ ;\quad c = -33{\cdot}58\ .$$

Solving equation (4.34) we find

$$n_4 = 11{\cdot}79\ .$$

(c) Since the difference in the values n_3 and n_4 is small, then the value for n_5 for the next, third, approximation cannot be calculated by formula (4.36), and we assume $n_5 = n_4$. With a small rounding-off $n_5 = 11{\cdot}80$.

We find $B_1 = 0{\cdot}850$, $B_2 = 0{\cdot}74$ according to the above-mentioned curves.

We determine the coefficients of equation (4.34):

$$a = 1{\cdot}048\ ;\quad b = -9{\cdot}582\ ;\quad c = -33{\cdot}60\ .$$

Solving equation (4.34) we obtain $n_6 = 11{\cdot}84$;

(d) For the true value of n we assume

$$n = \frac{n_5 + n_6}{2} = \frac{11{\cdot}80 + 11{\cdot}84}{2} = 11{\cdot}82\,.$$

3. Solving the small sequence of equations given in Section 18, we find the partial pressures of the components of the combustion products under dissociation conditions. The values of the equilibrium constants are taken from Table 2 of the Appendix.

The bulk of the calculations in this and succeeding examples is carried out on a 50 cm logarithmic slide rule. For comparison, in the right-hand column are shown the partial pressures of the combustion products of this same fuel, determined by the accurate method, using a calculating machine. The data from the calculations by both methods agree so closely between themselves that the expediency of using the proposed method in the given case leaves no room for doubt.

It can be seen from Example 1 that the pressure of the combustion products as a result of dissociation increased by 1·336 atm. Should the calculation of the chemical composition be carried out at another temperature, then the increase in pressure of the combustion products and the total pressure of the dissociated combustion products should correspond to this new temperature and would differ from the values given in the table. In the next example we shall show the sequences of the calculation of the chemical composition of the combustion products for a specified pressure of the dissociated combustion products p .

Sequence of calculation	Values of partial pressures of gases, atm	Values of partial pressures of gases as a result of calculation by accurate method, atm	Sequence of calculation	Values of partial pressures of gases, atm	Values of partial pressures of gases as a result of calculation by accurate method, atm
$b' = 0{\cdot}5(K_3 n + K_4)$	0·6766		p_O	0·068	0·0682
$a' = n + 1$	12·82		$\sqrt{p_{O_2}}$	0·579	
$c' = -0{\cdot}5\ X_H$	—26		p_{O_2}	0·335	0·3331
$\sqrt{p_{H_2}}$	1·397		p_{CO}	5·170	5·1801
p_{H_2}	1·952	1·960	p_{CO_2}	8·830	8·8199
p_{H_2O}	23·09	23·095			
p_{OH}	1·656	1·6545			
p_H	0·235	0·2356	Total pressure of combustion products	41·336	41·3364

Example 2. To calculate the chemical composition of the combustion products of the same fuel as in Example 1, for a pressure of the dissociated mixture of combustion products $p = 40$ atm, and a temperature $T = 3000$ °K.

1. We determine the increase in pressure Δp of the combustion products as a result of dissociation, corresponding to a pressure of the dissociated combustion products $p = 40$ atm.

With this objective :

(a) We find the parameters $\Delta i_{H,v,\Phi}$ for $a = 0{\cdot}8945$ by the method of graphical interpolation from the data of the curves in Figs. 10 and 11 of the Appendix. In the given case a supplementary graph need not be constructed, since $a = 0{\cdot}8945$ is extremely close to $a = 0{\cdot}90$. Assuming that $\Delta i_{H,v,\Phi}$ over the region from $a = 0{\cdot}80$ to $a = 0{\cdot}90$ depends linearly on a, we find its value for $a = 0{\cdot}8945$ from the relationship

$$\frac{0{\cdot}90 - 0{\cdot}80}{0{\cdot}90 - 0{\cdot}8945} = \frac{(\Delta i_{H,v,\Phi})_{0\cdot 90} - (\Delta i_{H,v,\Phi})_{0\cdot 80}}{(\Delta i_{H,v,\Phi})_{0\cdot 90} - (\Delta i_{H,v,\Phi})_{0\cdot 8945}} .$$

We find $\Delta i_{H,v,\Phi} = 596$ from the curves in Fig. 10 of the Appendix for $a = 0{\cdot}90$.

According to the curves in Fig. 11 of the Appendix we find $\Delta i_{L,v,\Phi} = 412$ for $a = 0{\cdot}80$.

Substituting these values in the equation written above, we obtain, for $a = 0{\cdot}8945$ the parameter $\Delta i_{H,v,\Phi} = 586$;

(b) $m_H = 2{\cdot}95$ is found from the curves in Fig. 7 of the Appendix (the parameter m_H is independent of the excess oxygen coefficient);

(c) We determine $\Delta i_{L,v,\Phi}$ for $a = 0{\cdot}8945$ and we find n_{eff} from formula (2.41). The method of determining $\Delta i_{L,v,\Phi}$ for a given value of a is similar to the method of determining the parameter $\Delta i_{H,v,\Phi}$ (in the example given, n_{eff} need not be determined, since the pressure of the dissociated mixture $p = 40$ atm is equal to that pressure for which the curves in Figs. 9–14 of the Appendix are constructed, and the necessity for interpolation of the quantity Δp with respect to pressure is eliminated);

(d) We find Δp for $a = 0{\cdot}8945$ according to equation (4.37):

$$\Delta p = \frac{p}{130 \times 40} \Delta i_{H,v,\Phi} \left(\frac{p_H}{p}\right)^{n_{\text{eff}}} \left(\frac{T - 2200}{T_{H,\Phi} - 2200}\right)^{m_H}.$$

In our case,

$$p = 40 \text{ atm}; \quad \Delta i_{H,v,\Phi} = 586; \quad p_{H,\Phi} = 40 \text{ atm};$$

$$T_{H,\Phi} = 3400^\circ\text{K}; \quad T = 3000^\circ\text{K}; \quad m_H = 2{\cdot}95.$$

Substituting the values of the parameters in equation (4.37), we obtain

$$\Delta p = 1{\cdot}362 \text{ atm}.$$

2. We determine the pressure of the undissociated combustion products:

$$p_T^0 = p - \Delta p;$$

$$p_T^0 = 40 - 1{\cdot}362 = 38{\cdot}638 \text{ atm}.$$

3. We find the independent parameters:

$$X_{C_T} = 14 \frac{38{\cdot}638}{40} = 13{\cdot}52;$$

$$X_{H_T} = 52 \frac{38{\cdot}638}{40} = 50{\cdot}23;$$

$$X_{O_T} = 48.34 \frac{38{\cdot}638}{40} = 46.70;$$

$$A_5 = 2 \times 13{\cdot}52 + 0{\cdot}5 \times 50{\cdot}23 - 46{\cdot}70 = 5{\cdot}462.$$

4. The problem is further solved according to the scheme discussed in Example 1. In our case the calculation of the ratio n is facilitated by the circumstance that the value $n = 11{\cdot}82$ is known to us for the same fuel for $p = 41{\cdot}336$ (see Example 1). Since $p = 40$ atm here, then it may be expected that the ratio of the partial pressure of water vapour to the partial pressure of diatomic hydrogen will be somewhat less than the value 11·82.

(a) As a first approximation we take

$$n_1 = 11{\cdot}50 \, .$$

We find from the curves in Fig. 27 of the Appendix for $0{\cdot}5\, X_{\mathrm{H}_T} = 25{\cdot}12$ that $B_1 = 0{\cdot}825$.

We find from the curves in Fig. 28 of the Appendix for $0{\cdot}5\, X_{\mathrm{N}_T} = 0$ that $B_2 = 0{\cdot}700$.

The coefficients $a = 1{\cdot}010$; $b = -9{\cdot}273$; $c = -32{\cdot}478$ are determined by the usual formula.

From equation (4.34) we find

$$n_2 = 11{\cdot}88 \, .$$

From formula (4.36) we find n_3 for the second approximation:

$$n_3 = \frac{2}{3} \times 11{\cdot}88 + \frac{1}{3} \times 11{\cdot}50 :$$

$$n_3 = 11{\cdot}72 \simeq 11{\cdot}70 \, .$$

From the curves in Fig. 27 of the Appendix we determine

$$B_1 = 0{\cdot}832 \, .$$

From the curves in Fig. 28 of the Appendix we find $B_2 = 0{\cdot}730$. We determine the coefficients:

$$a = 1{\cdot}01 \; ; \; b = -9{\cdot}232 \; ; \; c = -32{\cdot}448 \, .$$

Solving equation (4.34) we find $n_4 = 11{\cdot}78$.

(b) From formula (4.36) we finally establish

$$n = \frac{2}{3} \times 11{\cdot}78 + \frac{1}{3} \times 11{\cdot}70 \, ;$$

$$n = 11{\cdot}75 \, .$$

5. For $n = 11{\cdot}75$ we determine the partial pressures of the combustion products at $T = 3000°K$ and $p = 40$ atm.

Sequence of calculation	Values of partial pressures of gases, atm	Sequence of calculation	Values of partial pressures of gases, atm
$b' = 0{\cdot}5\,(K_3 n + K_4)$	0·6731	p_O	0·0678
$a' = n + 1$	12·75	$\sqrt{p_{O_2}}$	0·575
$c' = -0{\cdot}5\,X_H$	−25·12	p_{O_2}	0·331
$\sqrt{p_{H_2}}$	1·378	p_{CO}	5·015
p_{H_2O}	22·32	p_{CO_2}	8·505
p_{OH}	1·625	Pressure of dissociated combustion products	39·996
p_H	0·232		

The result is so close to $p = 40$ atm that there is no need to carry out any conversions of the partial pressures of the combustion products to a pressure of 40 atm .

EXAMPLE 3. To calculate the composition of the combustion products of a fuel characterized by the parameters $X_C = 25$, $X_H = 8$, $X_N = 22$ for $a = 0{\cdot}9018$, $p^0 = 40$ atm, $T = 3000°K$.

1. We determine the ratio n_0 (in the absence of dissociation). With this objective the following preliminary calculations are successively carried out :

(a) We find the parameters

$$X_O = (2X_C + 0{\cdot}5X_H)\ ;$$

$$X_O = (2 \times 25 + 0{\cdot}5 \times 8) \times 0{\cdot}9018\ ;$$

$$X_O = 48{\cdot}69\ ;$$

$$A_5 = 2X_C - X_O + 0{\cdot}5X_H\ ;$$

$$A_5 = 2 \times 25 - 48{\cdot}69 + 0{\cdot}5 \times 8\ ;$$

$$A_5 = 5{\cdot}31.$$

(b) We determine the coefficients of the quadratic equation (4.34), assuming $B_1 = B_2 = 0$, and we find n_0 :

$$a = 0{\cdot}1445 \times 5{\cdot}31;$$
$$a = 0{\cdot}7672;$$
$$b = 5{\cdot}31 + 0{\cdot}1445(5{\cdot}31 - 4) - 25;$$
$$b = -19{\cdot}501;$$
$$c = (5{\cdot}31 - 4) - 25\,;$$
$$c = -23{\cdot}69;$$

$$n_0 = \frac{19{\cdot}501 + \sqrt{[(-19{\cdot}501)^2 + 4\times 0{\cdot}7672\times 23{\cdot}69]}}{2\times 0{\cdot}7672},$$

$$n_0 = 26{\cdot}6.$$

2. We determine the ratio n for the given conditions:

(a) As a first approximation we choose $n_1 = 20$.

We find $B_1 = 0{\cdot}412$ from the curves in Fig. 27 of the Appendix.

We find $B_2 = 2{\cdot}44$ from the curves in Fig. 28 of the Appendix.

We determine the coefficients of the equation:

$$a = 1{\cdot}180\,;\ b = -16{\cdot}296;\ c = -21{\cdot}25.$$

We find $n_2 = 15{\cdot}02$ according to equation (4.34);

(b) As a second approximation we determine n_3 according to formula (4.36):

$$n_3 = \frac{2}{3}\times 15{\cdot}02 + \frac{1}{3}\times 20\,;$$

$$n_3 = 16{\cdot}67\,.$$

We round off at $n_3 = 17{\cdot}0$.

We find $B_1 = 0{\cdot}382$ from the curves in Fig. 27 of the Appendix.

We find $B_2 = 1{\cdot}83$ from the curves in Fig. 28 of the Appendix.

We determine the coefficients of the equation:

$$a = 1{\cdot}087;\ b = -17{\cdot}024;\ c = -21{\cdot}86\,.$$

We find $n_4 = 16{\cdot}85$;

(c) As a third approximation we find n_5 from formula (4.36):

$$n_5 = \frac{2}{3}\times 16{\cdot}85 + \frac{1}{3}\times 17\,;$$

$$n_5 = 16{\cdot}90\,.$$

From the curves in Fig. 27 of the Appendix we find $B_1 = 0{\cdot}381$.

From the curves in Fig. 28 of the Appendix we find $B_2 = 1{\cdot}82$.

We determine the coefficients:

$$a = 1{\cdot}086;\ b = -17{\cdot}037;\ c = -21{\cdot}87\,.$$

We find $n_6 = 16{\cdot}89$ according to equation (4·34) .

Finally we choose $n = 16{\cdot}89$.

For $n = 16{\cdot}89$ we find the partial pressures of the combustion products

Sequence of calculation	Values of partial pressures of gases, atm	Values of partial pressures of gases as a result of calculation by precise method, atm	Sequence of calculation	Values of partial pressures of gases, atm	Values of partial pressures of gases as a result of calculation by precise method, atm
$b' = 0{\cdot}5(K_3 n + K_4)$	0·931	—	p_{O_2}	0·685	0·6868
$a' = n + 1$	17·89	—	p_{CO}	7·260	7·257
$c' = -0{\cdot}5X_H$	− 4	—	p_{CO_2}	17·740	17·743
$\sqrt{p_{H_2}}$	0·4472	—	$\sqrt{p_{N_2}}$	3·288	—
p_{H_2}	0·20	0·200	p_{NO}	0·3372	0·3388
p_{H_2O}	3·380	3·384	p_N	0·0049	0·0049
p_{OH}	0·7580	0·7577	p_{N_2}	10·829	10·883
p_O	0·0974	0·0976	Pressure of dissociated combustion products	41·367	41·425
$\sqrt{p_{O_2}}$	0·828				

In the right-hand column are shown for comparison the calculations of the chemical composition of the combustion products of this fuel, carried out by a precise method. The results of the calculations by both methods and in the example are practically identical.

Example 4. To calculate the chemical composition of the combustion products of the same fuel as that in Example 3, for a pressure of the dissociated combustion products $p = 40$ atm and temperature $T = 3000\,°K$.

1. We determine the increase in pressure p corresponding to the pressure of the dissociated combustion products $p = 40$ atm .

(a) We find the parameter $\Delta i_{H,v\Phi}$ for $a = 0{\cdot}9018$.

Since $a = 0{\cdot}9018$ is very close to $a = 0{\cdot}90$, the value of $\Delta i_{H,v,\Phi}$ for $a = 0{\cdot}9018$ can be found from the relationship:

$$\frac{0{\cdot}95 - 0{\cdot}90}{0{\cdot}9018 - 0{\cdot}90} = \frac{(\Delta i_{H,v,\Phi})_{0\cdot95} - (\Delta i_{H,v,\Phi})_{0\cdot90}}{(\Delta i_{H,v,\Phi})_{0\cdot9018} - (\Delta i_{H,v,\Phi})_{0\cdot90}} .$$

Having determined, from the nomograms in Figs. 9 and 10 of the Appendix the quantities

$$(\Delta i_{H, v, \Phi})_{0\cdot95} = 755;$$

$$(\Delta i_{H, v, \Phi})_{0\cdot90} = 596\ ,$$

we find

$$(\Delta i_{H, v, \Phi})_{0\cdot9018} = 602;$$

(b) We find m_H from the curves in Fig. 7 of the Appendix

$$m_H = 2\cdot90;$$

(c) Δp is determined from equation (4.37):

$$\Delta p = 1\cdot488\ .$$

2. We find the pressure of the undissociated combustion products p_T^0:

$$p_T^0 = 40 - 1\cdot488;$$

$$p_T^0 = 38\cdot512 \text{ atm}\ .$$

3. We find the parameters

$$X_{C_T} = 25\,\frac{38\cdot512}{40} = 24\cdot08\ ;$$

$$X_{H_T} = 8\,\frac{38\cdot512}{40} = 7\cdot705\ ;$$

$$X_{N_T} = 22\,\frac{38\cdot512}{40} = 21\cdot19\ ;$$

$$X_{O_T} = 48\cdot69\,\frac{38\cdot512}{40} = 46\cdot90\ ;$$

$$A_5 = 2 \times 24\cdot08 + \frac{7.705}{2} - 46\cdot90 = 5\cdot112.$$

4. In Example 3 for the same fuel, but for $p^0 = 40$ atm, we obtained $n = 16\cdot89$. It can be expected that in our case the value of n is somewhat less, since the total pressure of the combustion products has been reduced.

(a) We try $n_1 = 16\cdot80$.

From the curves in Fig. 27 of the Appendix, for $0\cdot5X_{H_T} = 3\cdot852$ we find $B_1 = 0\cdot373$.

From the curves in Fig. 28 of the Appendix, for $0\cdot5X_{N_T} = 10\cdot60$ we find $B_2 = 1\cdot78$.

We determine the coefficients of the equation:

$$a = 1{\cdot}051;\ b = -16{\cdot}375;\ c = -21{\cdot}04.$$

Solving equation (4.34) we obtain

$$n_2 = 16{\cdot}77\ .$$

Finally we take $n = 16{\cdot}78$.

5. For $n = 16{\cdot}78$ we determine the partial pressures of the combustion products.

Sequence of calculation	Values of partial pressures of gases, atm	Values of partial pressures of gases after conversion, atm	Sequence of calculation	Values of partial pressures of gases, atm	Values of partial pressures of gases after conversion atm
$b' = 0{\cdot}5(K_3 n + K_4)$	0·925	—	p_{O_2}	0·676	0·678
$a' = n + 1$	17·78	—	p_{CO}	7·030	7·052
$c' = -0{\cdot}5X_H$	− 3·852	—	p_{CO_2}	17·050	17·110
$\sqrt{p_{H_2}}$	0·4392	—	$\sqrt{p_{N_2}}$	3·226	—
p_{H_2}	0·1930	0·1936	p_{NO}	0·3287	0·3300
p_{H_2O}	3·239	3·2500	p_N	0·0048	0·0048
p_{OH}	0·7400	0·7420	p_{N_2}	10·428	10·475
p_H	0·0740	0·0742	Pressure of dissociated combustion products	39·8607	40·000
p_{O_2}	0·0968	0·0973			
$\sqrt{p_{O_2}}$	0·822	—			

The pressure of the combustion products was obtained as equal to 39·8607 atm. In view of the fact that the difference in the values 40 and 39·8607 atm is extremely small, it is not necessary to repeat the caculation.

In this case, each one of the partial pressures can be multiplied by the ratio 40/39·8607 , assuming that there is the same linear dependence of the partial pressures of each one of the components on the total pressure of the combustion products. The results of the conversion are given in the right-hand column.

20. Calculation of the Enthalpy of the Combustible, Oxidant and Fuel

The enthalpy of the combustible, oxidant and fuel on the whole should be presented in the same system of reading principles which is adopted for the enthalpy of the combustion products.

We shall denote the proportion by weight of combustible and oxidant in 1 kg of fuel by q_c and q_o, and their enthalpies in kcal/kg by i_c and i_o respectively. By the law of additivity, the total enthalpy of 1 kg of fuel i_f is:

$$i_f = i_c\, q_c + i_o\, q_o\,. \tag{1}$$

The numerical values of the enthalpy of the combustible and oxidant can be determined either via the heat of combustion of these substances Q_{comb}, or via their heats of formation Q_{form}, the values of which are determined from the handbooks.

We shall show the method of calculating the enthalpy of a substance for a known value of the heat of combustion Q_{comb}. By heat of combustion is understood the quantity of heat liberated as a result of the complete combustion of organic compounds in oxygen. For this it is assumed that the process takes place at the same pressure at the commencement and termination of the combustion, and that the temperature of the combustion products is equal to the temperature of the starting material. The values of the heat of combustion of substances is usually given in the handbooks for a temperature of +20°C, or a value close to it (+18, +25 °C).

The quantity of heat liberated by the conditions of combustion of the substance mentioned above, will be equal to the difference in enthalpy of the fuel and of the combustion products:

$$Q_{comb} = i + i_{O_2} - i_{c\cdot p}\,, \tag{2}$$

whence

$$i = Q_{comb} + i_{c\cdot p} - i_{O_2}\,. \tag{3}$$

Here i is the enthalpy of the substance at that temperature for which the heat of combustion Q_{comb} is determined;

Q_{comb} is the heat of combustion of the substance (determined from the handbooks);

$i_{c\cdot p}$ is the total enthalpy of the combustion products;

i_{O_2} is the enthalpy of oxygen.

The values of the enthalpy of the individual components of the combustion products required for calculating $i_{c\cdot p}$, and also the enthalpy of oxygen i_{O_2}, are found from a table of enthalpy of combustion products for the same temperature at which the heat of combustion Q_{comb} is determined.

EXAMPLE 1. To determine the enthalpy of kerosene (empirical formula $C_{7\cdot233}H_{13\cdot2}$) for a given heat of combustion at 20°C ($T = 293$°K) $Q_{comb} = 11{,}000$ kcal/kg $= 1100$ kcal/mole (for an empirical mole of kerosene equal to 100 g).

We write down the equation for the complete combustion of kerosene in oxygen:

$$C_{7\cdot233}H_{13\cdot2} + 10\cdot535\ O_2 = 7\cdot233\ CO_2 + 6\cdot6H_2O\ .$$

According to Table 1 of the Appendix, we find, for 20°C

$$I_{O_2} = 2\cdot03 \text{ kcal/mole};$$

$$I_{CO_2} = 2\cdot18 \text{ kcal/mole};$$

$$\underset{\text{(water vapour)}}{I_{H_2O}} = 2\cdot31 \text{ kcal/mole}.$$

The enthalpy of water in the liquid state is determined according to the formula

$$I_{H_2O} = \underset{\text{(water vapour)}}{I_{H_2O}} + Q_{vap}\ ,$$

where Q_{vap} is the heat of vaporization of water at the given temperature, equal to —10·57 kcal/mole.

Consequently, the enthalpy of the water is

$$I_{H_2O} = 2\cdot31 - 10\cdot07 = -8\cdot26 \text{ kcal/mole}.$$

The enthalpy of kerosene is determined according to formula (3):

$$i_{ker} = 1100 + 7\cdot233 \times 2\cdot18 + 6\cdot6(-8\cdot26) - 10\cdot533 \times 2\cdot03;$$

$$i_{ker} = 1039\cdot9 \text{ kcal/mole} = 10{,}399 \text{ kcal/kg}.$$

We shall show the method of calculating the enthalpy of a substance for a known value of the heat of formation Q_{form}. The numerical value of Q_{form} depends on the state of the initial elements, which form the given substance. In order to determine the value of Q_{form} these elements are considered as existing in some standard state, i.e. in a state in which they are most widely distributed in nature. As the standard state of hydrogen, nitrogen and oxygen, we take their state in the form of the molecular gases H_2, N_2 and O_2.

Carbon is assumed to be in the form of solid graphite.

The values of the heat of formation of substances from elements existing in the standard state are given in the handbooks. The sign of the heat of formation will be determined from the following considerations: if in the formation of the given substance heat is expended, then Q_{form} is assumed to have a negative value; if, however, the reaction for the formation of the substance from its elements, existing in the standard state, is accompanied by the liberation of heat, then Q_{form} is assumed to have a positive value. Since in certain tables there can be a contradictory interpretation of the sign of the heat of formation, then prior to determining the enthalpy of the substance, it is essential to establish if heat is liberated or absorbed as a result of the reaction taking place with formation of the substance, and to attribute the parameter Q_{form} correspondingly with a positive or negative sign.

The enthalpy of a substance can be defined as the difference between the enthalpy of its constituent chemical elements and the heat of formation (taken with the appropriate sign):

$$i = i_e - Q_{\text{form}}. \tag{4}$$

Here i is the enthalpy of the substance;
i_e is the total enthalpy of the chemical elements in their standard state;
Q_{form} is the heat of formation in kcal/mole (determined from the handbooks).

The enthalpy of the chemical elements oxygen, nitrogen, hydrogen and carbon in the standard state ($T = 293$°K) for the adopted system of principles of reading enthalpies is given in the following table.

Name of elements	Enthalpy	
	kcal/mole	kcal/kg
Oxygen (O_2)	2·03	63·6
Nitrogen (N_2)	2·03	72·5
Hydrogen (H_2)	59·09	29·300
Carbon (β-graphite)	94·23	7·884

EXAMPLE 2. To determine the enthalpy of nitric acid HNO_3 if its heat of formation is known

$$Q_{\text{form}} = 41{\cdot}66 \text{ kcal/mole}.$$

In accordance with formula (4)

$$i_{HNO_3} = \frac{1}{2} I_{H_2} + \frac{1}{2} I_{N_2} + \frac{3}{2} I_{O_2} - Q_{form} =$$
$$= \frac{1}{2} \times 59{\cdot}09 + \frac{1}{2} \times 2{\cdot}03 + \frac{3}{2} \times 2{\cdot}03 - 41{\cdot}66 =$$
$$= -8{\cdot}06 \text{ kcal/mole} = -128 \text{ kcal/kg}.$$

In the case when the temperature of the combustible or oxidant on entry into the combustion chamber of the engine is noticeably different from the temperature at which the parameters Q_{comb} or Q_{form} are determined, it is necessary to take this circumstance into account, correspondingly reducing or increasing the enthalpy of the combustible or oxidant. In changing the aggregate state of the substance relative to the state for which the calculation of the enthalpy is carried out according to formula (3) or (4), it is necessary to take into account the heat of transition from one state into the other.

The enthalpy of the fuel can be also determined by the formula

$$i_f = \frac{i_c + \nu i_O}{i + \nu}. \tag{5}$$

In Tables 4 and 5 of the Appendix, certain physico-chemical properties are given for the more well-known oxidants and combustibles[10].

REFERENCES

1. G. N., Abramovich, *Applied Gas Dynamics (Prikladnaya gazovaya dinamika)*, Gostekhizdat, 1951.
2. A. V. Bolgarskii and V. K. Shchukin, *Operating Processes in Liquid Propellant Engines (Rabochiye protsessy v zhidkostno reaktivnykh dvigatelyakh)*, Oborongiz, 1953.
3. P. Wenner, *Thermochemical Calculations (Termokhimicheskie raschety)*, Foreign Literature Publishing House, M. 1950.
4. V. P. Glushko, *Liquid Fuel for Jet Engines, (Zhidkoye toplivo dlya reaktivnykh dvigatelei)*, Vol. I, published by the Air Force Institute of Aviation (to Zhukovskii) 1936.
5. B. Lewis and G. Elbe, *Combustion, Flames and Explosions of Gases, (*Academic Press Inc. New York, 1951.
6. D. Sutton, *Rocket Engines (Raketnye dvigateli)*, Foreign Literature Publishing House, 1952.
7. G. B., Sinyarev and M. V. Dobrovol'skii, *Liquid Propellant Rocket Engines (Zhidkostnyye raketnyye dvigateli)*, Oborongiz, 1957.
8. N. G., Chernyshev, *Chemistry of Rocket Fuels (Khimiya raketnykh topliv)*, Oborongiz, 1949.
9. *Thermodynamic Terminology (Terminologiya termodinamiki)*, Academy of Sciences USSR, 1952.
10. G. B. Sinyarev and M. V. Dobrovols'kii, *Liquid Propellant Rocket Engines (Zhidkostnyye raketnyye dvigateli)*, Oborongiz, 1957.

TABLE 1

Enthalpy of Gases I, kcal/mole

T °K	H_2	O_2	N_2	CO	NO	OH	CO_2	H_2O	H	O	N
0	57·113	0	0	66·760	21·400	34·444	0	0	79·797	58·68	84·61
300	59·149	2·082	2·085	68·845	23·612	36·563	2·256	2·387	81·286	60·170	86·100
400	59·843	2·792	2·781	69·543	24·326	37·272	3·197	3·203	81·783	60·666	86·596
600	61·241	4·280	4·198	70·969	25·788	38·684	5·327	4·879	82·776	61·659	87·589
800	62·649	5·854	5·667	72·459	27·321	40·102	7·696	6·662	83·769	62·652	88·582
1000	64·077	7·497	7·202	74·016	28·920	41·548	10·233	8·563	84·762	63·645	89·575
1200	65·540	9·185	8·793	75·628	30·569	43·027	12·886	10·583	85·755	64·638	90·568
1400	67·044	10·903	10·426	77·281	32·254	44·564	15·624	12·700	86·748	65·631	91·561
1600	68·584	12·654	12·090	78·963	33·967	46·147	18·424	14·918	87·741	66·624	92·554
1800	70·166	14·427	13·782	80·669	35·699	47·759	21·273	17·230	88·734	67·617	93·547
2000	71·785	16·220	15·500	82·397	37·447	49·401	24·159	19·622	89·727	68·610	94·540
2200	73·436	18·036	17·226	84·140	39·208	51·068	27·072	22·069	90·720	69·603	95·533
2400	75·113	19·876	18·966	85·891	40·980	52·775	30·014	24·566	91·713	70·596	96·526
2600	76·822	21·734	20·714	87·649	42·761	54·498	32·983	27·109	92·706	71·589	97·519
2800	78·555	23·610	22·475	89·417	44·549	56·240	35·967	29·686	93·699	72·582	98·512
3000	80·302	25·502	24·245	91·194	46·343	58·009	38·970	32·288	94·692	73·575	99·505
3200	82·061	27·416	26·023	92·975	48·142	59·799	41·987	34·910	95·685	74·568	100·498
3400	83·828	29·348	27·796	94·756	49·948	61·599	45·015	37·547	96·677	75·560	101·490
3600	85·606	31·299	29·576	96·536	51·800	63·409	48·056	40·197	97·671	76·554	102·480
3800	87·388	33·263	31·376	98·308	53·600	65·222	51·104	42·850	98·664	77·547	103·470

TABLE 2

Chemical Equilibrium Constants

T °K	$K=\dfrac{p_{CO_2}p_{H_2}}{p_{CO}p_{H_2O}}$	$K_1=\dfrac{p_{CO}\sqrt{p_O}}{p_{CO_2}}$	$K_2=\dfrac{p_{H_2}\sqrt{p_{O_2}}}{p_{H_2O}}$	$K_3=\dfrac{p_{OH}\sqrt{p_{H_2}}}{p_{H_2O}}$	$K_4=\dfrac{p_H}{\sqrt{p_{H_2}}}$	$K_5=\dfrac{p_O}{\sqrt{p_{O_2}}}$	$K_6=\dfrac{p_N}{\sqrt{p_{N_2}}}$	$K_7=\dfrac{p_{NO}}{\sqrt{p_{N_2}}\sqrt{p_{O_2}}}$
300	88520·0	—	—	—	—	—	—	—
400	1469·0	—	—	—	—	—	—	—
600	27·10	—	—	—	—	—	—	—
800	4·074	—	—	—	—	—	—	0·000006
1000	1·403	—	—	—	—	—	—	0·000089
1200	0·7162	—	—	—	—	—	—	0·000541
1400	0·4560	0·000001	—	—	0·000006	0·000001	—	0·001968
1600	0·3273	0·000019	0·000006	0·000006	0·000061	0·000016	—	0·005188
1800	0·2630	0·000204	0·000054	0·000065	0·000397	0·000130	—	0·01099
2000	0·2198	0·001375	0·000302	0·000398	0·001787	0·000710	—	0·02018
2200	0·1919	0·006413	0·001231	0·001820	0·006138	0·002845	0·000007	0·03319
2400	0·1730	0·02250	0·003891	0·006457	0·01720	0·009142	0·000038	0·05012
2600	0·1607	0·06223	0·01	0·01820	0·04126	0·02433	0·000158	0·07080
2800	0·1517	0·1546	0·02345	0·04571	0·08760	0·05656	0·000525	0·09572
3000	0·1445	0·3389	0·04898	0·1003	0·1683	0·1178	0·001497	0·1239
3200	0·1400	0·6668	0·09333	0·2065	0·2982	0·2265	0·003759	0·1560
3400	0·1343	1·208	0·1622	0·3793	0·4943	0·3972	0·008433	0·1901
3600	0·1301	2·049	0·2666	0·6362	0·777	0·6583	0·0170	0·234
3800	0·1273	3·282	0·4179	1·034	1·164	1·032	0·0265	0·280

TABLE 3

Entropy of Gases S, kcal/g-mol. deg C

T °K	H_2	O_2	N_2	CO	NO	OH	CO_2	H_2O	H	O	N
300	10·648	0	0	20·786	2·947	9·106	0	0	17·117	13·718	13·48
400	12·646	2·060	2·005	22·795	4·996	11·146	2·694	2·321	18·564	15·216	15·31
600	15·480	5·056	4·873	25·683	7·931	13·990	7·024	5·713	20·561	17·355	17·33
800	17·494	7·320	6·987	27·825	10·131	16·030	10·410	8·274	21·988	18·639	18·773
1000	19·100	9·153	8·699	29·562	11·915	17·648	13·230	10·391	23·106	19·932	19·67
1200	20·432	10·680	10·146	31·029	13·421	19·002	15·655	12·229	24·005	20·852	20·42
1400	21·580	11·990	11·403	32·310	14·723	20·192	17·720	13·870	24·777	21·611	21·22
1600	22·610	13·190	12·500	33·410	15·870	21·255	19·590	15·340	25·440	22·308	21·91
1800	23·55	14·25	13·516	34·430	16·900	22·21	21·280	16·710	26·026	22·912	22·48
2000	24·405	15·173	14·421	35·344	17·830	23·075	22·810	17·980	26·553	23·436	22·99
2200	25·170	16·050	15·241	36·140	18·650	23·870	24·160	19·160	27·016	23·921	23·41
2400	25·910	16·87	15·999	36·925	19·433	24·611	25·457	20·234	27·451	24·385	23·89
2600	26·600	17·570	16·699	37·650	20·150	25·300	26·660	21·240	27·857	24·759	24·30
2800	27·250	18·27	17·353	38·310	20·813	25·946	27·764	22·199	28·225	25·136	24·68
3000	27·850	18·930	17·964	38·909	21·432	26·556	28·800	23·100	28·566	25·491	25·01
3200	28·42	19·55	18·538	39·484	22·012	27·134	29·773	23·946	28·886	25·844	25·33
3400	28·96	20·14	19·078	40·024	22·559	27·679	30·691	24·745	29·187	26·144	25·62
3600	29·48	20·70	19·558	40·536	23·076	28·194	31·561	25·496	29·470	26·432	25·91
3800	29·98	21·23	20·043	41·02	23·567	28·685	32·386	26·21	29·740	26·706	26·19

TABLE 4

Physico-Chemical Properties of Certain Oxidants

Oxidant	Chemical formula	Molecular weight	Elementary Composition, kg/kg				Heat of formation Q_{form} kcal/g-mol	Specific gravity at 15° C	Freezing point, °C, at 1 atm	Boiling point, °C, at 1 atm
			O_o	C_o	H_o	N_o				
Nitric Acid	HNO_3	63·02	0·762	0	0·016	0·222	+41·66	1·52	− 41·6	+ 86
Nitrogen Tetroxide	N_2O_4	92·01	0·696	0	0	0·304	+ 6·80	1·47	− 11·2	+ 21
Tetranitromethane	$C(NO_2)_4$	196·03	0·663	0·061	0	0·286	− 8·80	1·65	+ 13	+126
Liquid Oxygen	O_2	32·00	1·000	0	0	0	0·00 (gas)	1·14 (at −183 °C)	−227	−183
Hydrogen Peroxide	H_2O_2	32·02	0·940	0	0·060	0	+44·84	1·46	− 2	+151
Liquid Water	H_2O	18·02	0·889	0	0·111	0	+68·35	1·00	0	+100

TABLE 5

Physico-Chemical Properties of Certain Combustibles

Combustible	Chemical formula	Molecular weight	Elementary Composition, kg/kg				Heat of formation Q_{form} kcal/g-mol	Specific gravity, at 15° C	Boiling point, °C at 1 atm	Freezing point, °C at 1 atm
			C_e	H_e	O_e	N_e				
Kerosene, tractor	Mixture of hydrocarbons	—	0·858	0·135	0·007	0	—	0·79—0·84	~170	— 60
Ethyl Alcohol	C_2H_5OH	46·04	0·522	0·131	0·347	0	+66·36	0·789	78·3	—117·3
Methyl Alcohol	CH_3OH	32·03	0·375	0·125	0·500	0	+57·02	0·791	64·6	— 94·9
Aniline	$C_6H_5NH_2$	93·08	0·774	0·076	0	0·150	— 7·09	1·022	184·4	— 6·2
Furfuryl Alcohol	$C_4H_3OCH_2OH$	98·06	0·614	0·061	0·325	0	+63·1	—	171	— 32
Triethylamine	$(C_2H_5)_3N$	101·07	0·712	0·149	0	0·139	+42·33	0·728	89·5	—114·8
Xylidene	$(CH_3)_2C_6H_3NH_2$	121·12	0·793	0·091	0	0·116	+46·2	0·98	210	— 54
Diethylamine	$C_4H_{11}N$	73·14	0 657	0·152	0	0·191	+29·3	0·70	56	— 50
Dimethylhydrazine	$(CH_3)_2N_2H_2$	62·12	0·400	0·134	0	0·466	—11·28	0·83	63	— 58
Hydrazine hydrate	$(NH_2)_2H_2O$	50·06	0	0·122	0·318	0·560	+63·15	1·03	118·5	— 40
Hydrazine	N_2H_4	32·03	0	0·125	0	0·875	—12·05	1·01	113·5	— 2
Ammonia	NH_3	17·03	0	0·177	0	0·823	+16·60	0·68	— 33	— 77

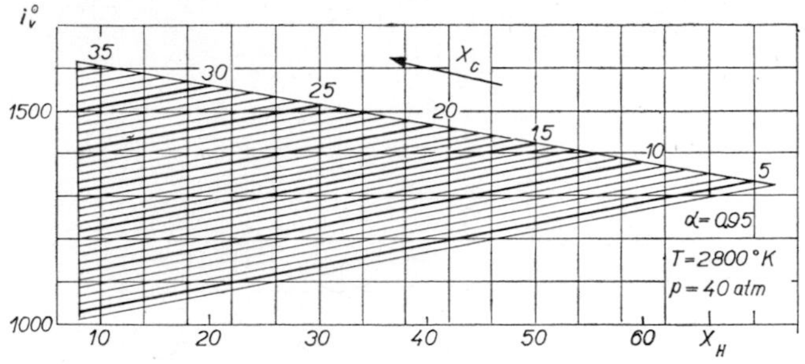

FIG. 1

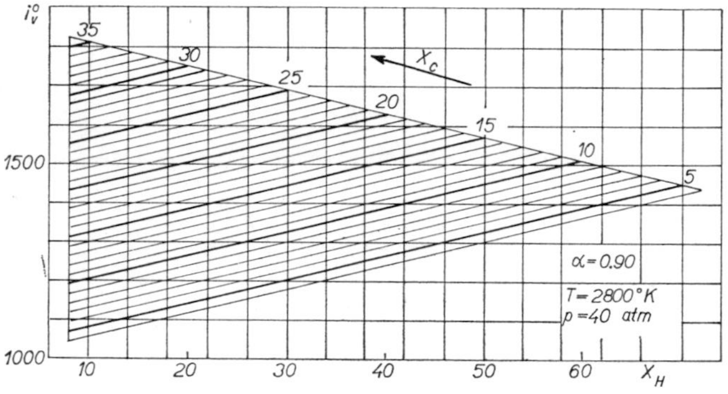

FIG. 2

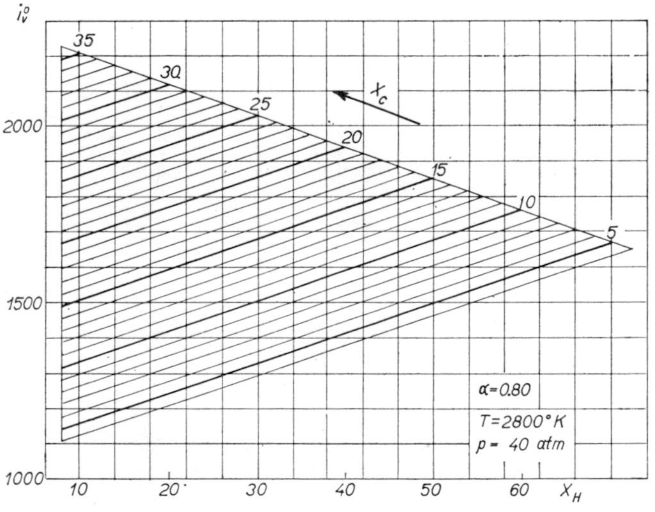

FIG. 3

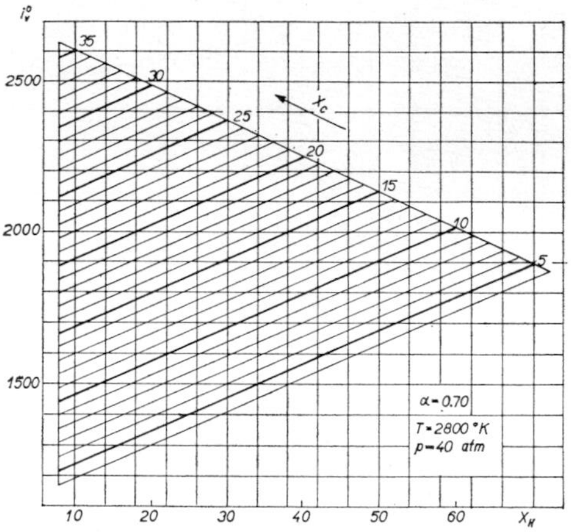
i_v^0
35
30
25
20
15
10
5
X_c
2500
2000
1500
α = 0.70
T = 2800 °K
p = 40 atm
10
20
30
40
50
60
X_H

Fig. 4

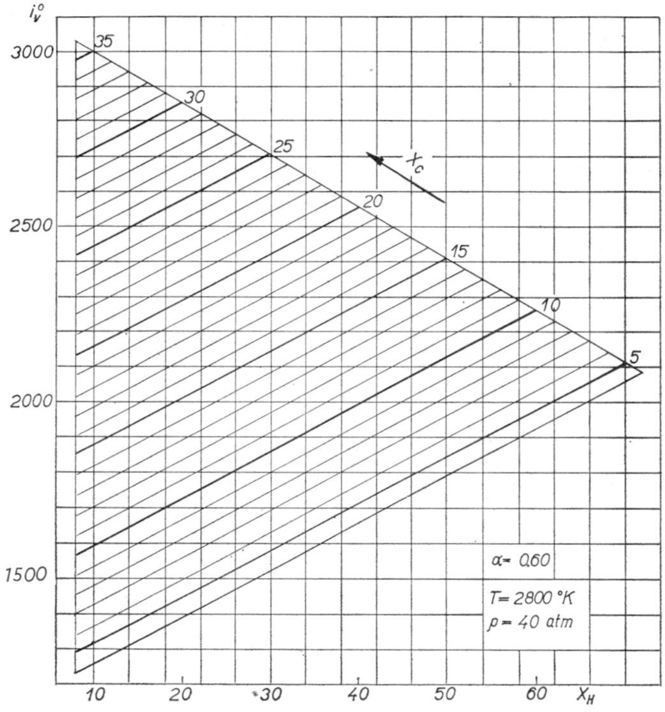
i_v^0
35
30
25
20
15
10
5
X_c
3000
2500
2000
1500
α = 0.60
T = 2800 °K
p = 40 atm
10
20
30
40
50
60
X_H

Fig. 5

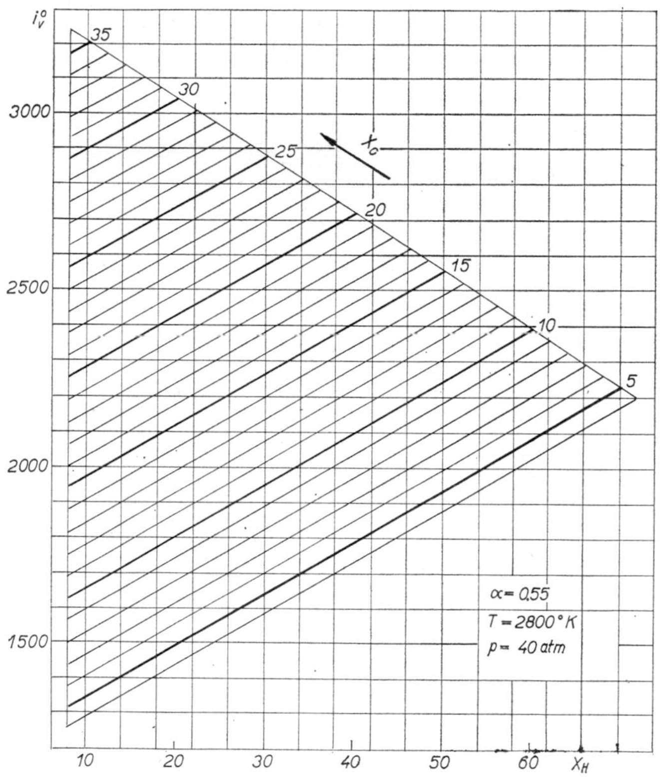
i_v^0
3000
2500
2000
1500
35
30
25
20
15
10
5
x_c
α = 0.55
T = 2800 °K
p = 40 atm
10
20
30
40
50
60
X_H

FIG. 6

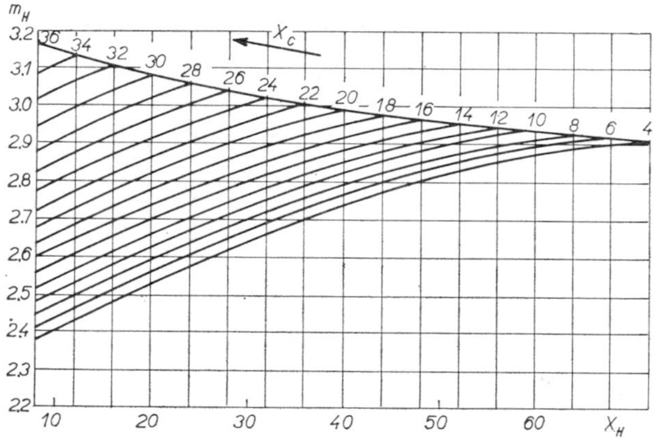
m_H
3.2
3.1
3.0
2.9
2.8
2.7
2.6
2.5
2.4
2.3
2.2
X_c
36
34
32
30
28
26
24
22
20
18
16
14
12
10
8
6
4
10
20
30
40
50
60
X_H

FIG. 7

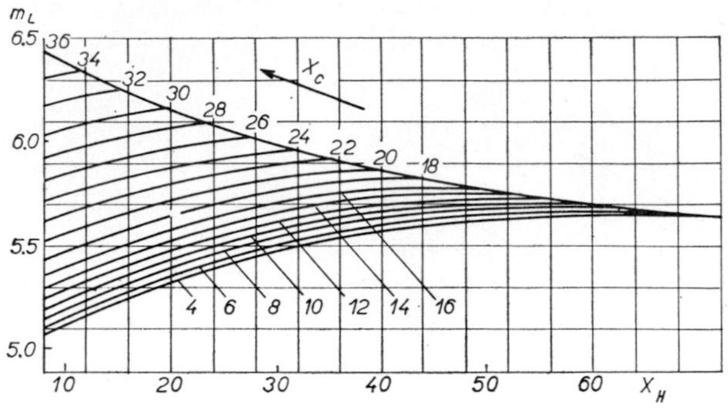
m_L
6.5
6.0
5.5
5.0
10
20
30
40
50
60
X_H
X_c
36
34
32
30
28
26
24
22
20
18
4
6
8
10
12
14
16

FIG. 8

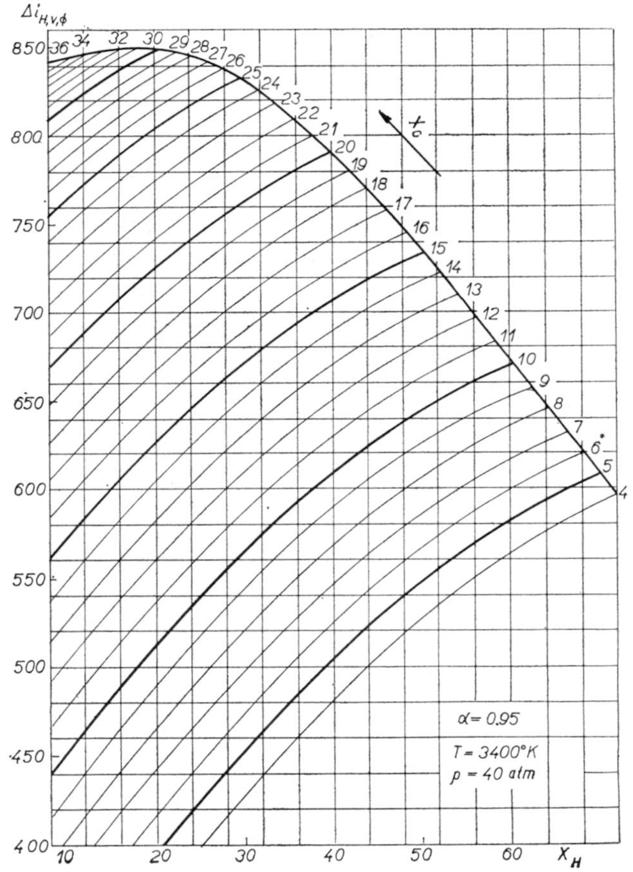
$\Delta i_{H,v,\phi}$
850
800
750
700
650
600
550
500
450
400
10
20
30
40
50
60
X_H
X_c
$\alpha = 0.95$
$T = 3400°K$
$p = 40$ atm

FIG. 9

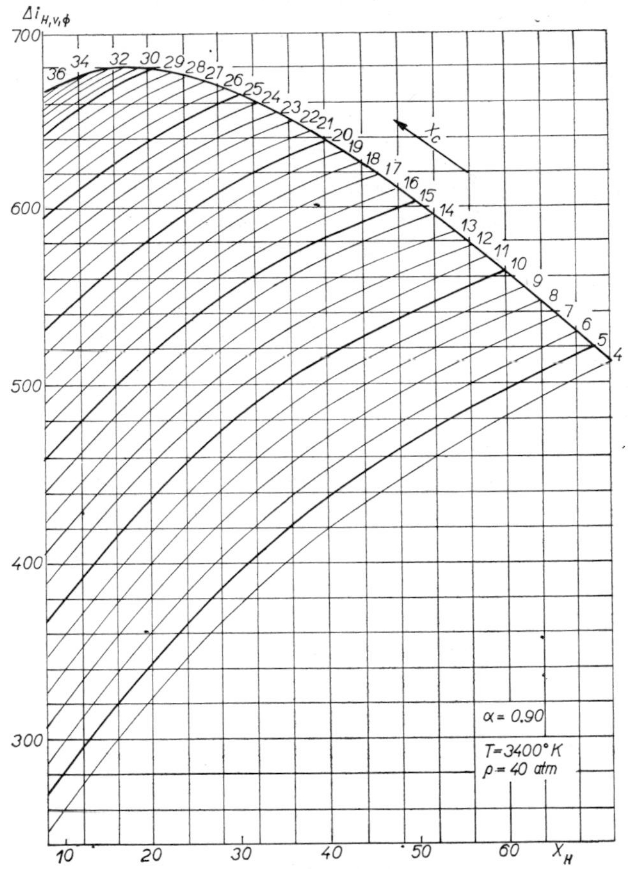
$\Delta i_{H,v,\phi}$
700
600
500
400
300
36
34
32
30
29
28
27
26
25
24
23
22
21
20
19
18
17
16
15
14
13
12
11
10
9
8
7
6
5
4
X_c
α = 0.90
T=3400° K
p = 40 atm
10
20
30
40
50
60
X_H

FIG. 10

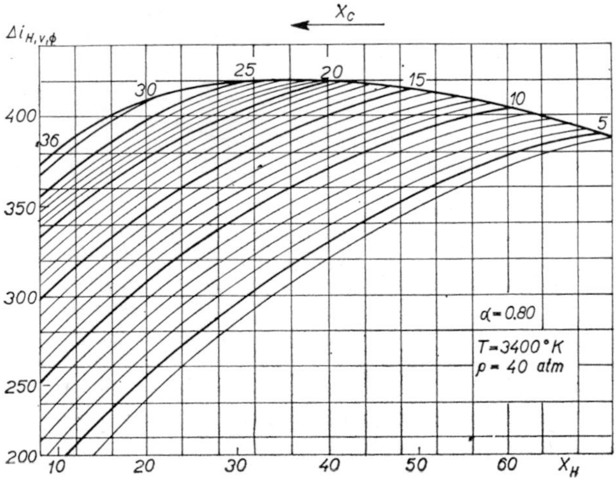
X_c
$\Delta i_{H,v,\phi}$
400
350
300
250
200
36
30
25
20
15
10
5
α = 0.80
T=3400° K
p = 40 atm
10
20
30
40
50
60
X_H

FIG. 11

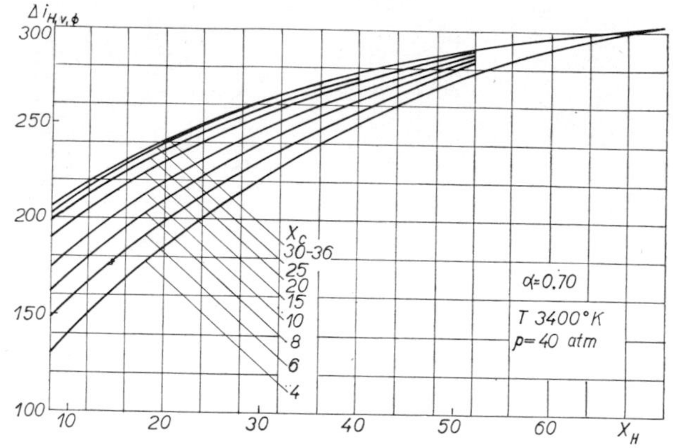

FIG. 12

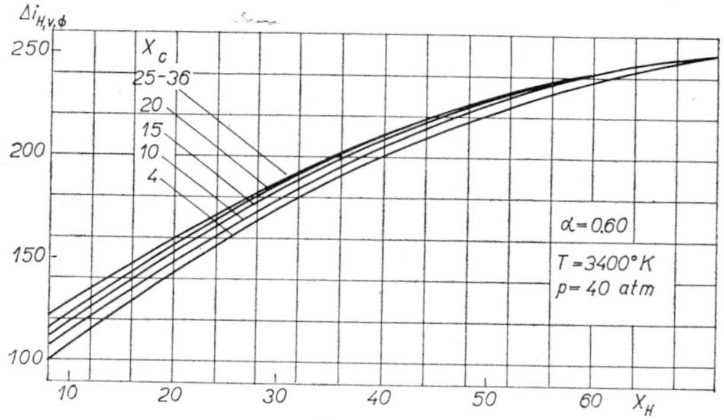

FIG. 13

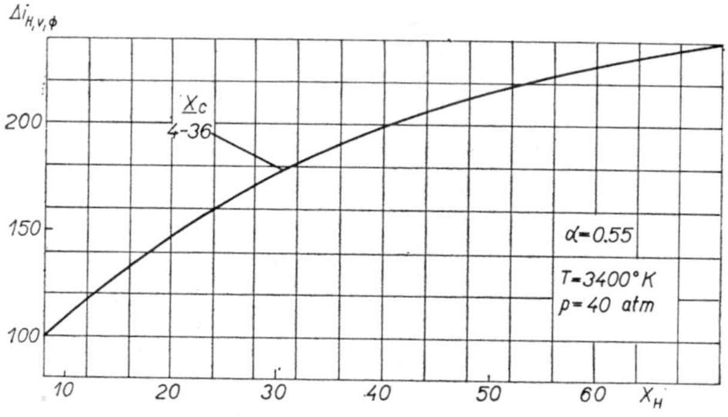

FIG. 14

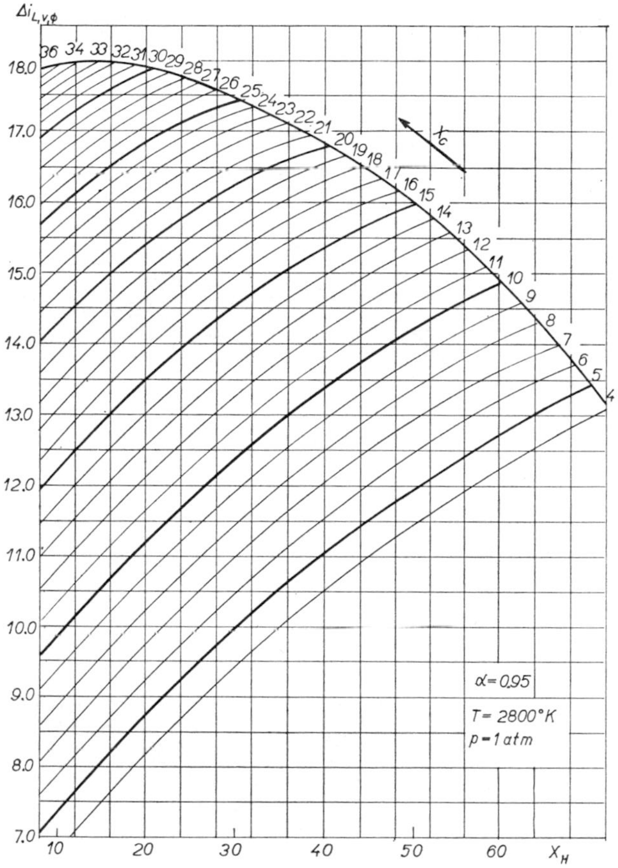

$\Delta i_{L,v,\phi}$
18.0
17.0
16.0
15.0
14.0
13.0
12.0
11.0
10.0
9.0
8.0
7.0
10
20
30
40
50
60
X_H
X_C
36 34 33 32 31 30 29 28 27 26 25 24 23 22 21 20 19 18 17 16 15 14 13 12 11 10 9 8 7 6 5 4
$\alpha = 0.95$
$T = 2800°K$
$p = 1$ atm

FIG. 15

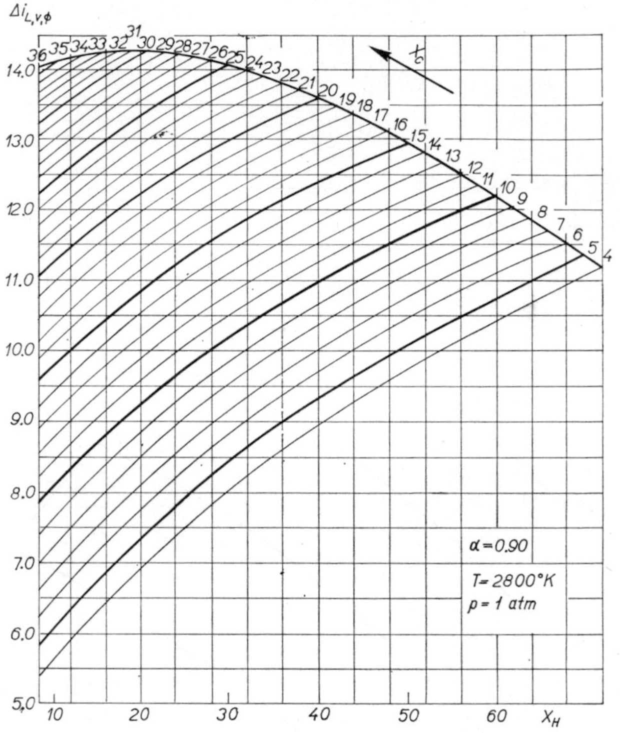
$\Delta i_{L,v,\phi}$
x_c
α=0.90
T=2800°K
p=1 atm
X_H

Fig. 16

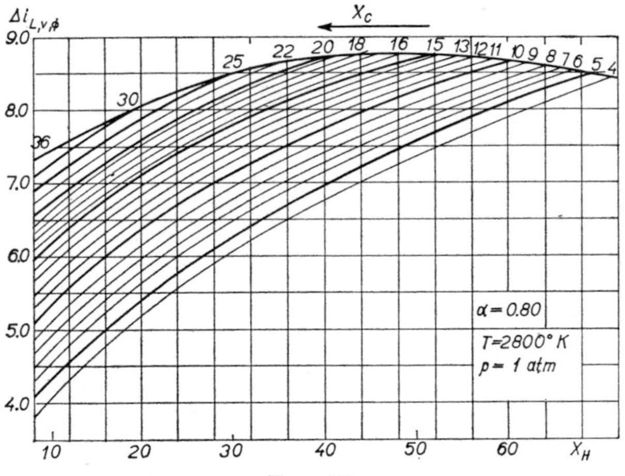
$\Delta i_{L,v,\phi}$
X_c
α=0.80
T=2800° K
p=1 atm
X_H

Fig. 17

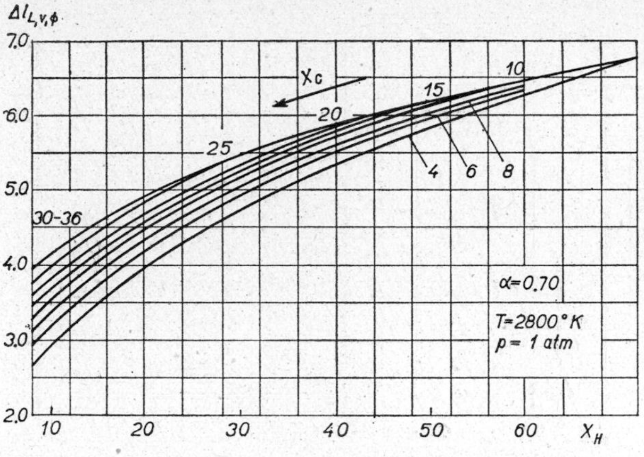

FIG. 18

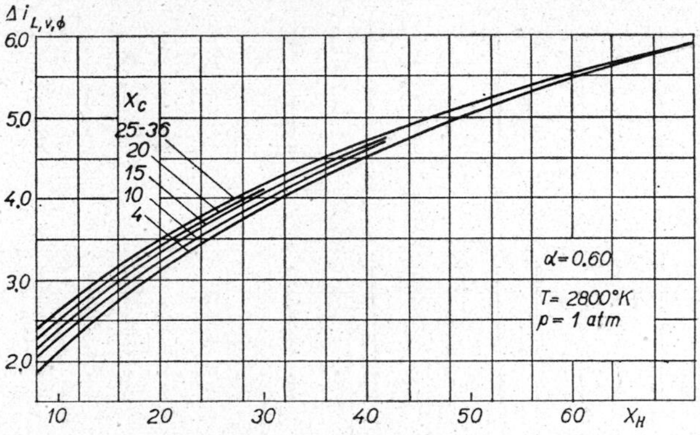

FIG. 19

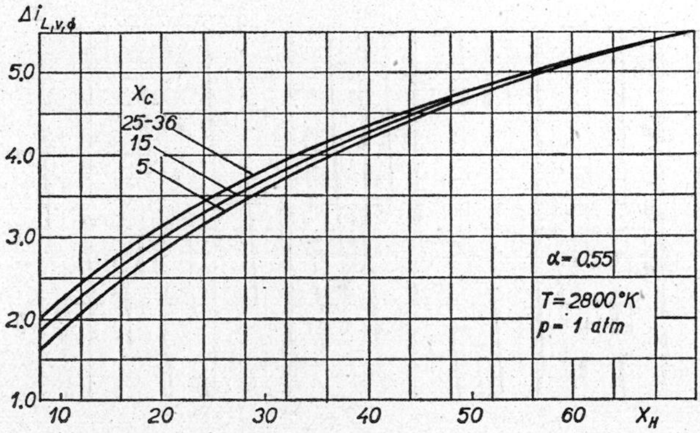

FIG. 20

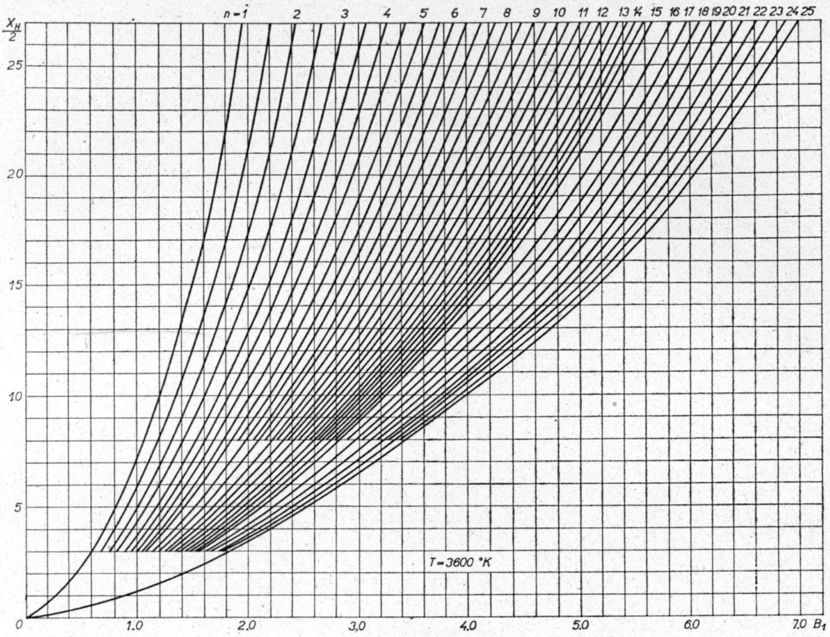
n = 1 2 3 4 5 6 7 8 9 10 11 12 13 14 15 16 17 18 19 20 21 22 23 24 25
$\frac{X_H}{2}$
25
20
15
10
5
0
1.0
2.0
3.0
4.0
5.0
6.0
7.0 B_1
T = 3600 °K

FIG. 21

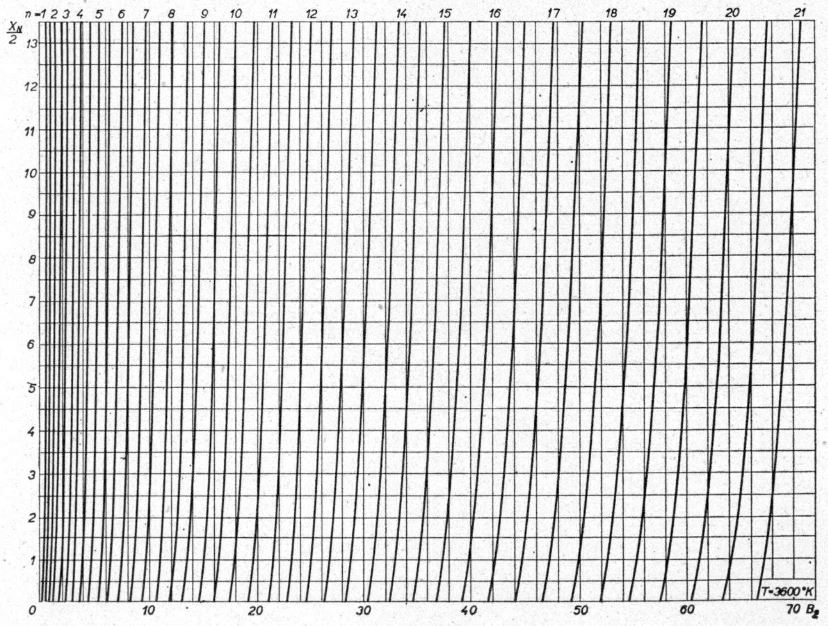
n = 1 2 3 4 5 6 7 8 9 10 11 12 13 14 15 16 17 18 19 20 21
$\frac{X_H}{2}$
13
12
11
10
9
8
7
6
5
4
3
2
1
0
10
20
30
40
50
60
70 B_2
T = 3600 °K

FIG. 22

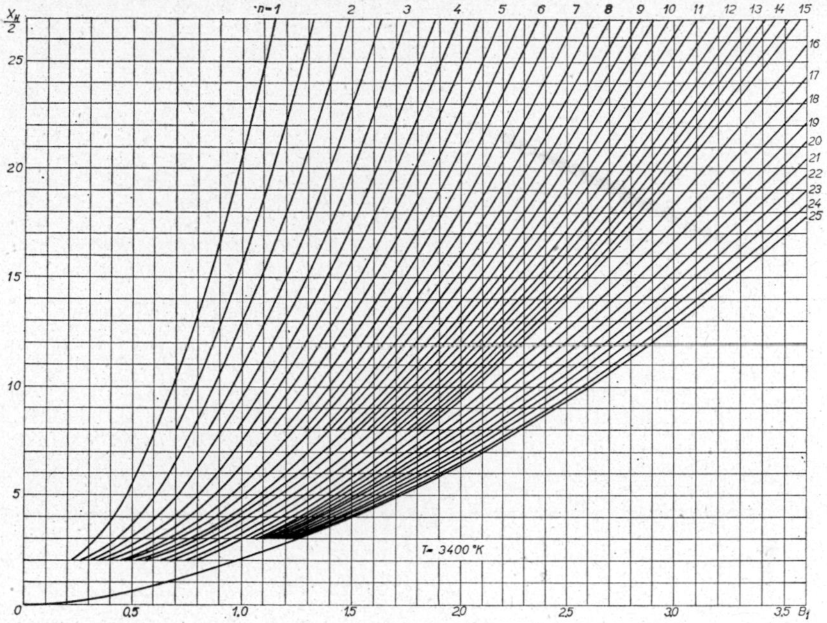
$\frac{X_N}{2}$
n=1
2
3
4
5
6
7
8
9
10
11
12
13
14
15
16
17
18
19
20
21
22
23
24
25
0
5
10
15
20
25
0,5
1,0
1,5
2,0
2,5
3,0
3,5
B_1
T= 3400 °K

FIG. 23

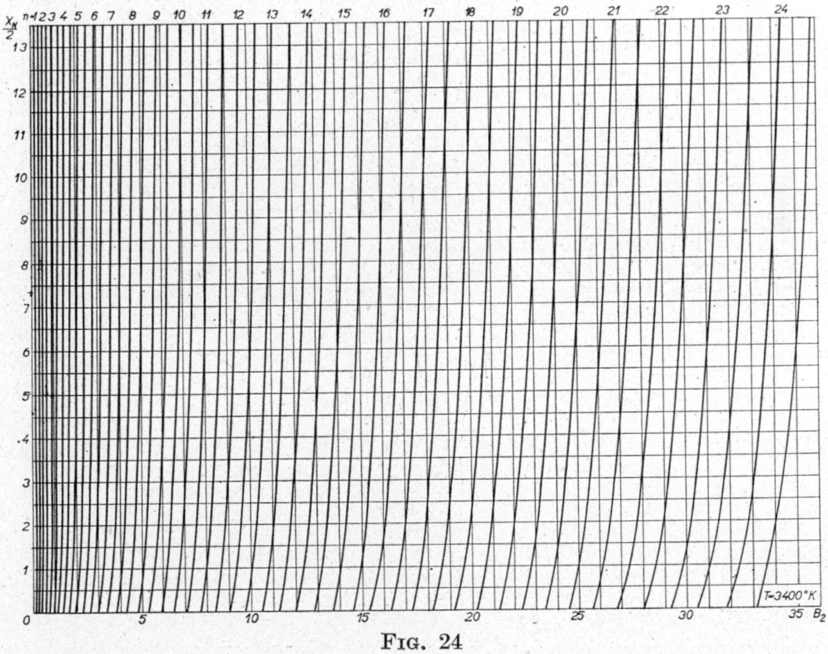
$\frac{X_N}{2}$
n=1 2 3 4 5 6 7 8 9 10 11 12 13 14 15 16 17 18 19 20 21 22 23 24
0
1
2
3
4
5
6
7
8
9
10
11
12
13
5
10
15
20
25
30
35
B_2
T=3400 °K

FIG. 24

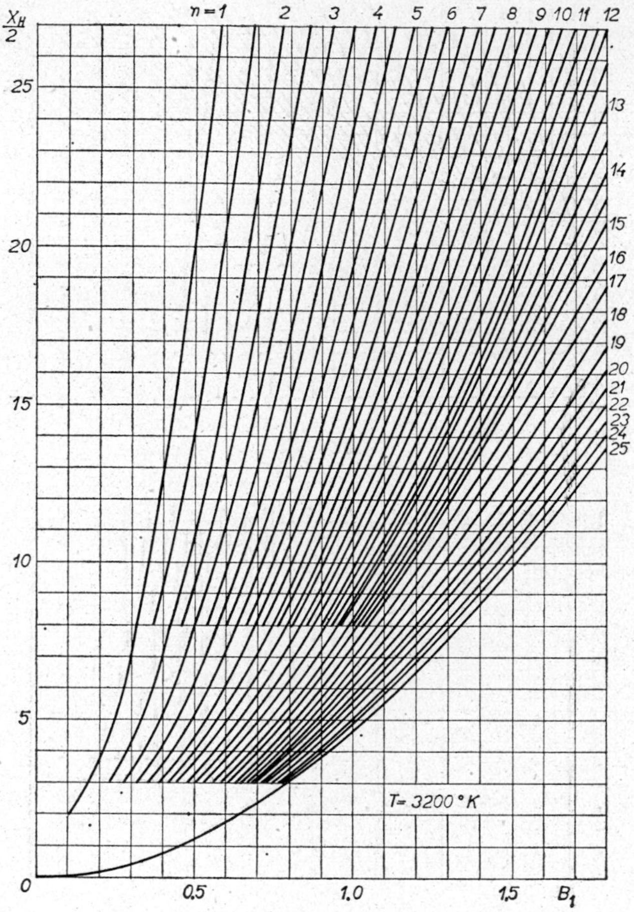

n=1
2
3
4
5
6
7
8
9
10
11
12
13
14
15
16
17
18
19
20
21
22
23
24
25
X_H/2
25
20
15
10
5
0
0.5
1.0
1.5
B_1
T= 3200 °K

FIG. 25

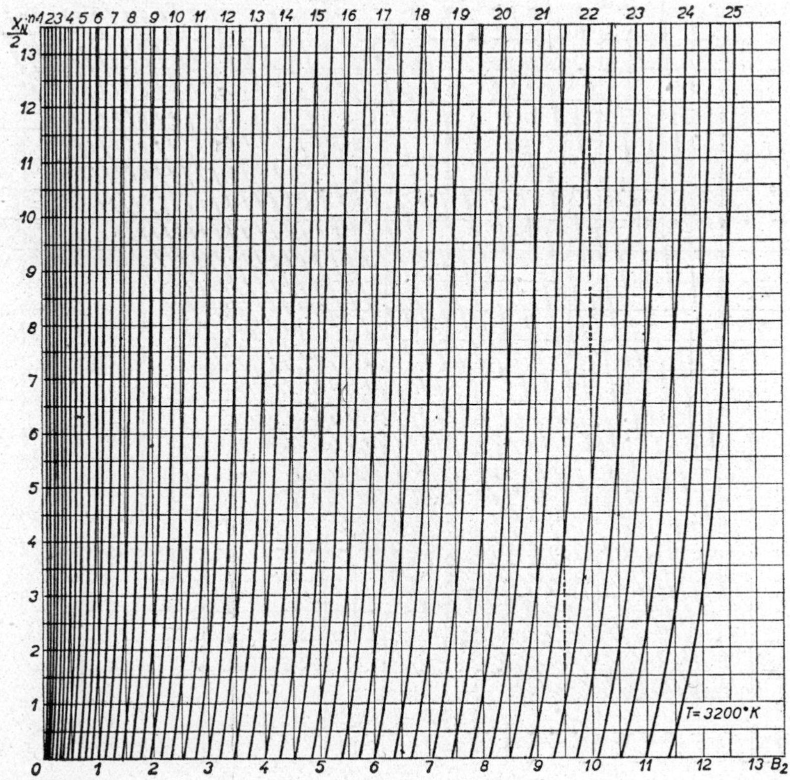
n=1 2 3 4 5 6 7 8 9 10 11 12 13 14 15 16 17 18 19 20 21 22 23 24 25
X_N/2
13
12
11
10
9
8
7
6
5
4
3
2
1
0
0 1 2 3 4 5 6 7 8 9 10 11 12 13 B_2
T= 3200°K

FIG. 26

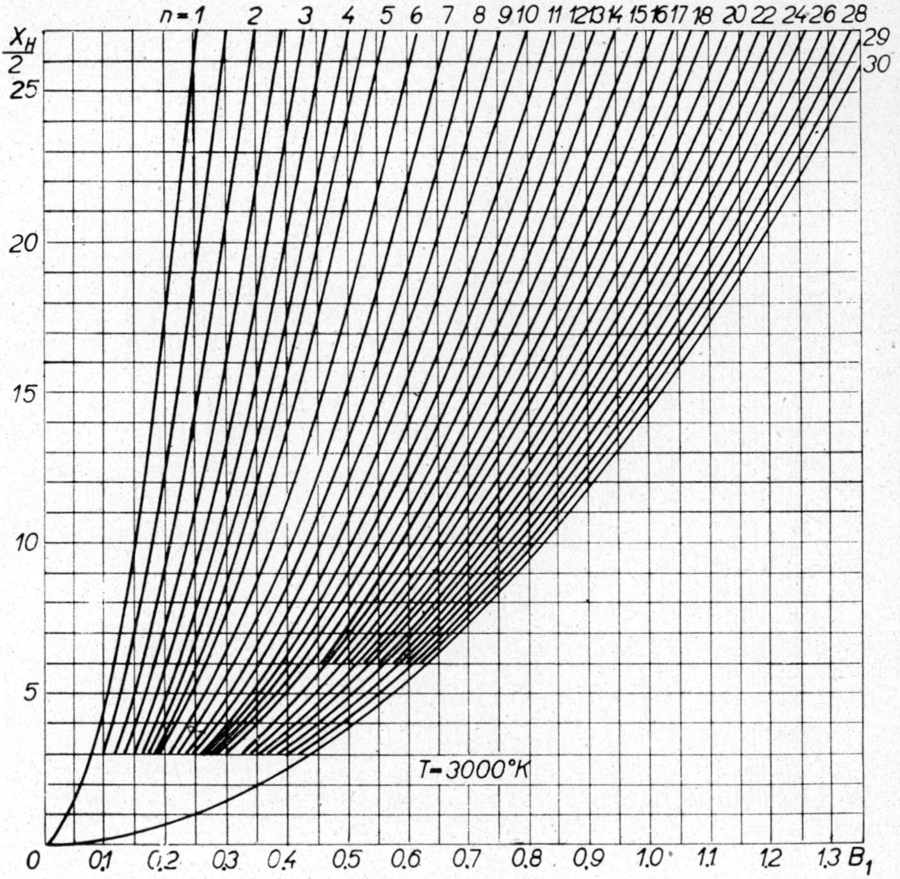
n = 1 2 3 4 5 6 7 8 9 10 11 12 13 14 15 16 17 18 20 22 24 26 28
29
30
X_H/2
25
20
15
10
5
0
0.1 0.2 0.3 0.4 0.5 0.6 0.7 0.8 0.9 1.0 1.1 1.2 1.3 B_1
T = 3000°K

FIG. 27

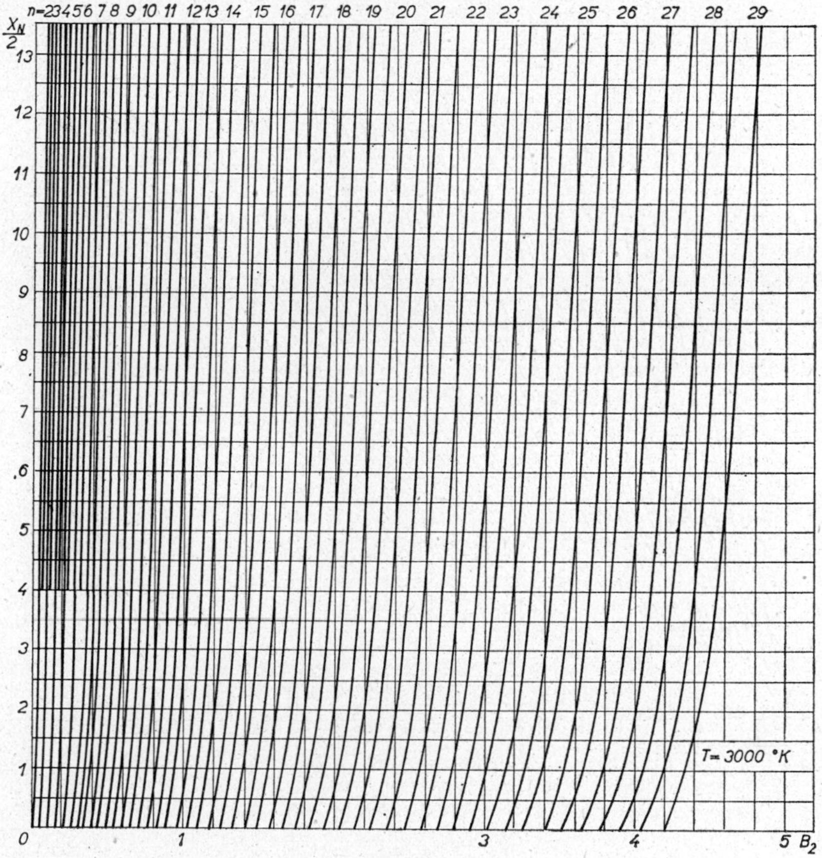

n=2 3 4 5 6 7 8 9 10 11 12 13 14 15 16 17 18 19 20 21 22 23 24 25 26 27 28 29
$\frac{X_N}{2}$
13
12
11
10
9
8
7
6
5
4
3
2
1
0
1
3
4
5 B_2
T= 3000 °K

FIG. 28

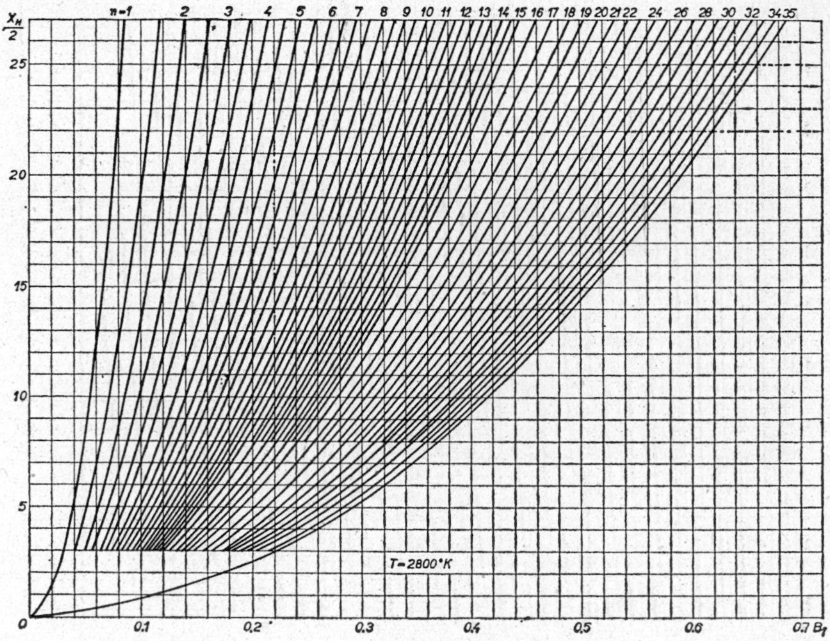
n=1
2
3
4
5
6
7
8
9
10
11
12
13
14
15
16
17
18
19
20
21
22
24
26
28
30
32
34
35
$\frac{X_H}{2}$
25
20
15
10
5
0
0.1
0.2
0.3
0.4
0.5
0.6
0.7
B_1
T=2800°K

FIG. 29

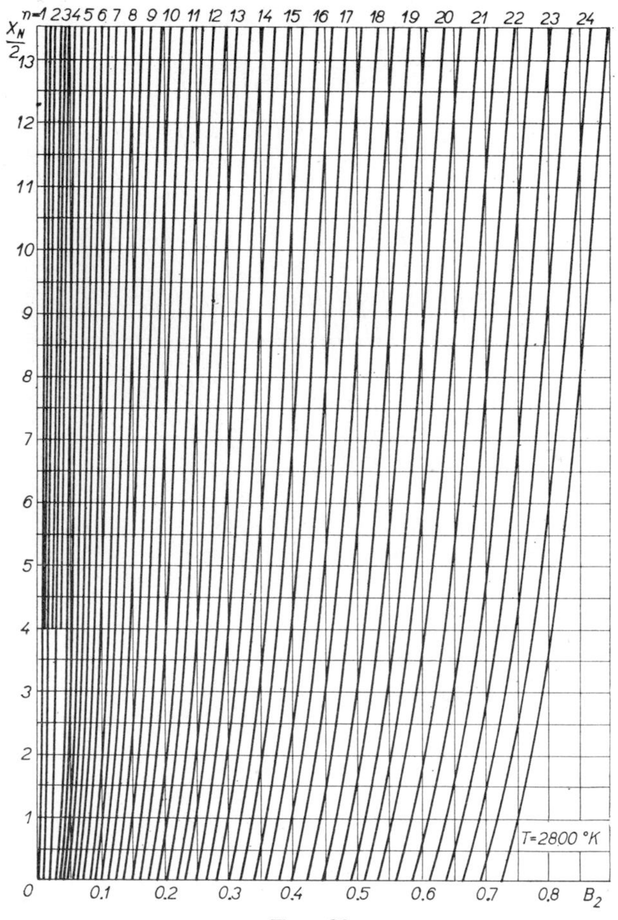
n=1 2 3 4 5 6 7 8 9 10 11 12 13 14 15 16 17 18 19 20 21 22 23 24
$\frac{X_N}{2}$
13
12
11
10
9
8
7
6
5
4
3
2
1
0
0.1
0.2
0.3
0.4
0.5
0.6
0.7
0.8
B_2
T=2800 °K

FIG. 30

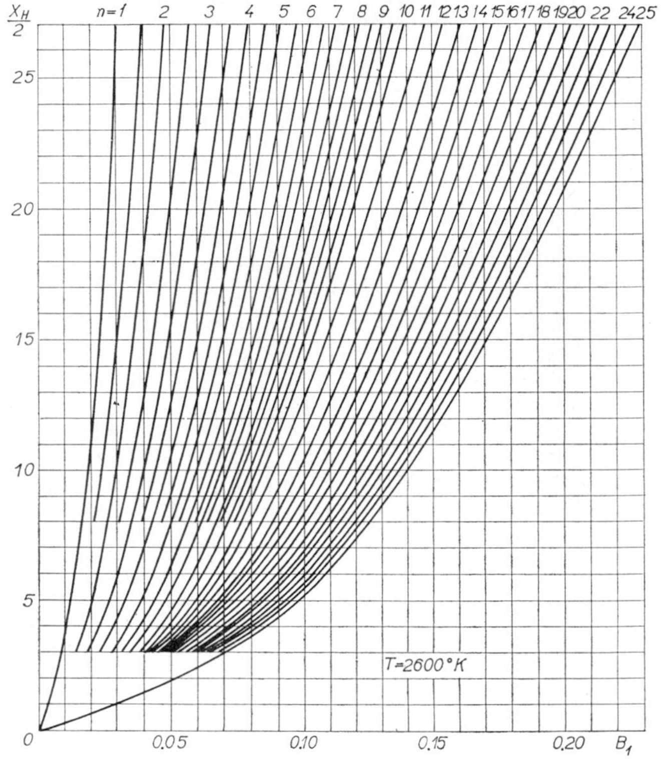

$\frac{X_H}{2}$
n=1 2 3 4 5 6 7 8 9 10 11 12 13 14 15 16 17 18 19 20 22 24 25
25
20
15
10
5
0
0.05
0.10
0.15
0.20
B_1
T=2600°K

FIG. 31

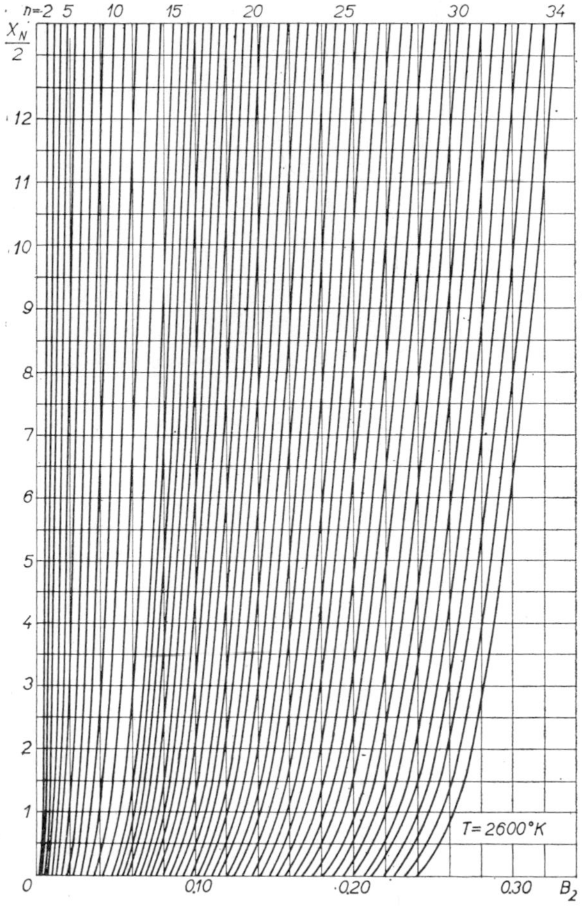

n=2 5 10 15 20 25 30 34
X_N/2
12
11
10
9
8
7
6
5
4
3
2
1
0
0,10
0,20
0,30
B_2
T=2600°K

Fig. 32

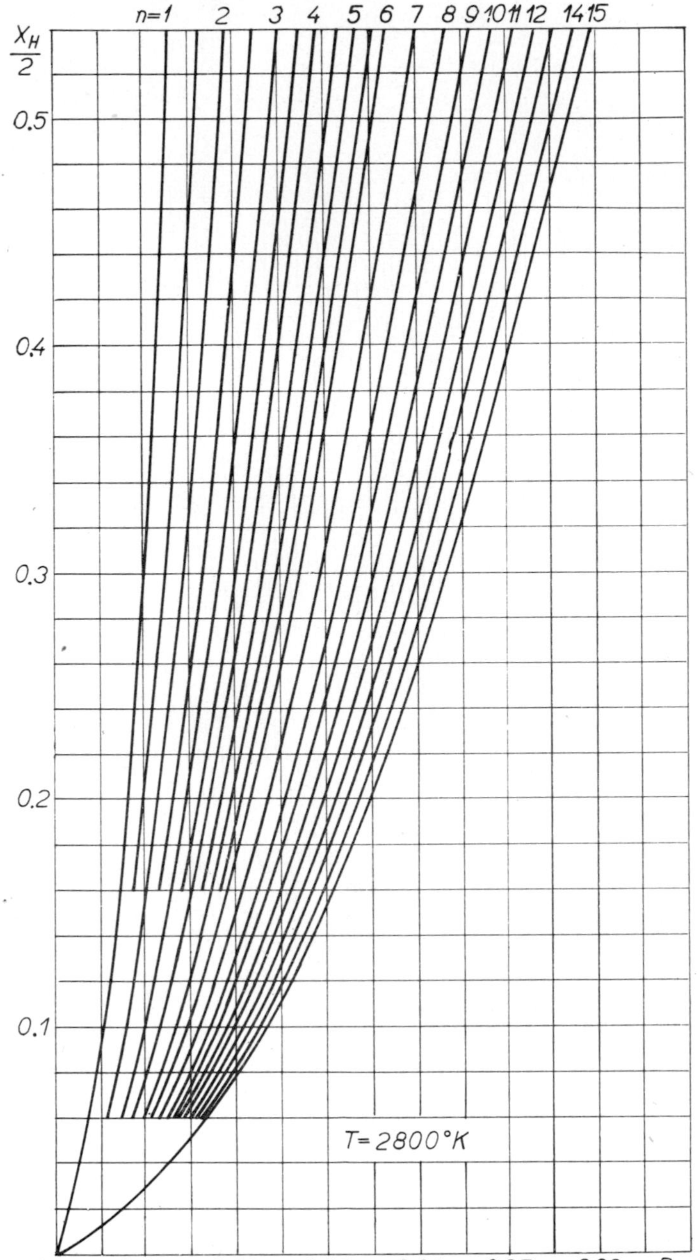
n=1
2
3
4
5
6
7
8
9
10
11
12
14
15
$\frac{X_H}{2}$
0.5
0.4
0.3
0.2
0.1
0
0.01
0.02
0.03
0.04
0.05
0.06
B_1
T= 2800°K

FIG. 33

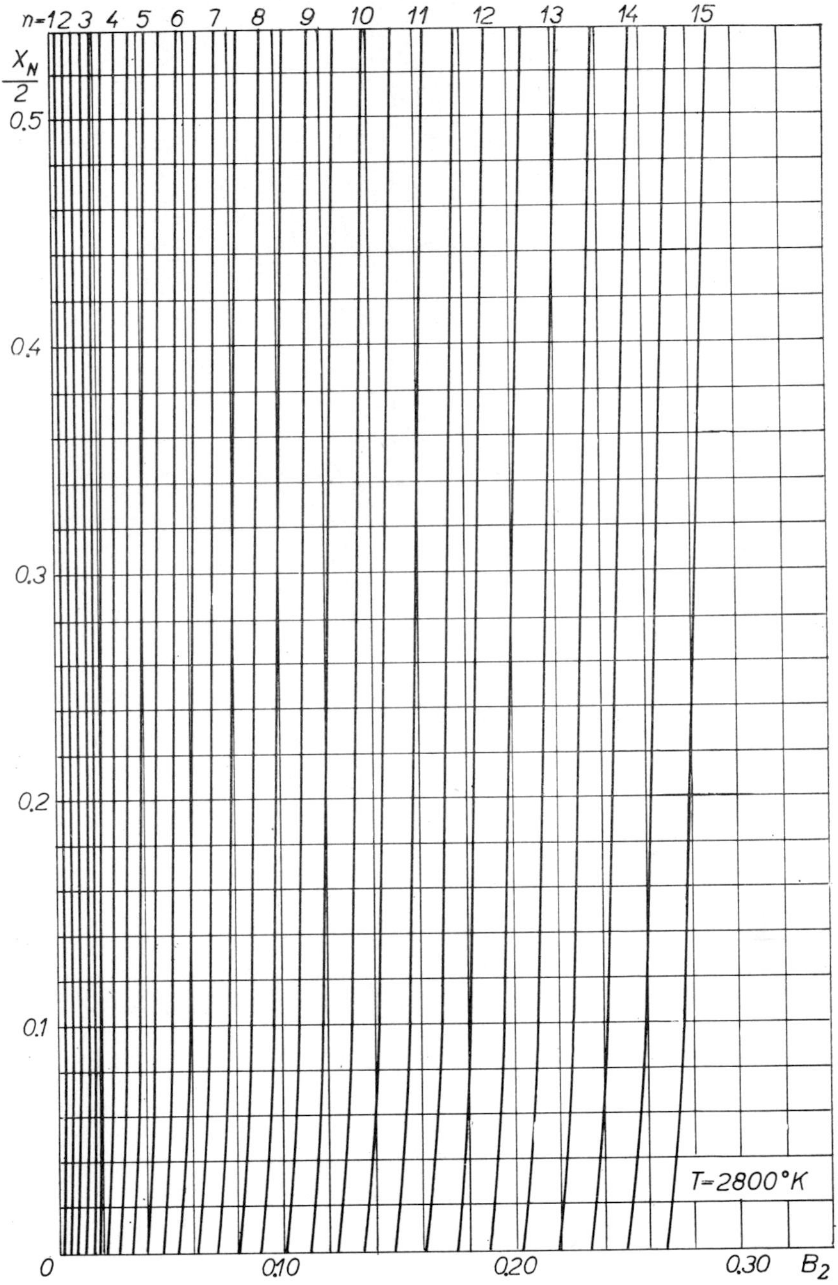
n=1 2 3 4 5 6 7 8 9 10 11 12 13 14 15
$\frac{X_N}{2}$
0.5
0.4
0.3
0.2
0.1
0
0.10
0.20
0.30
B_2
T=2800°K

FIG. 34

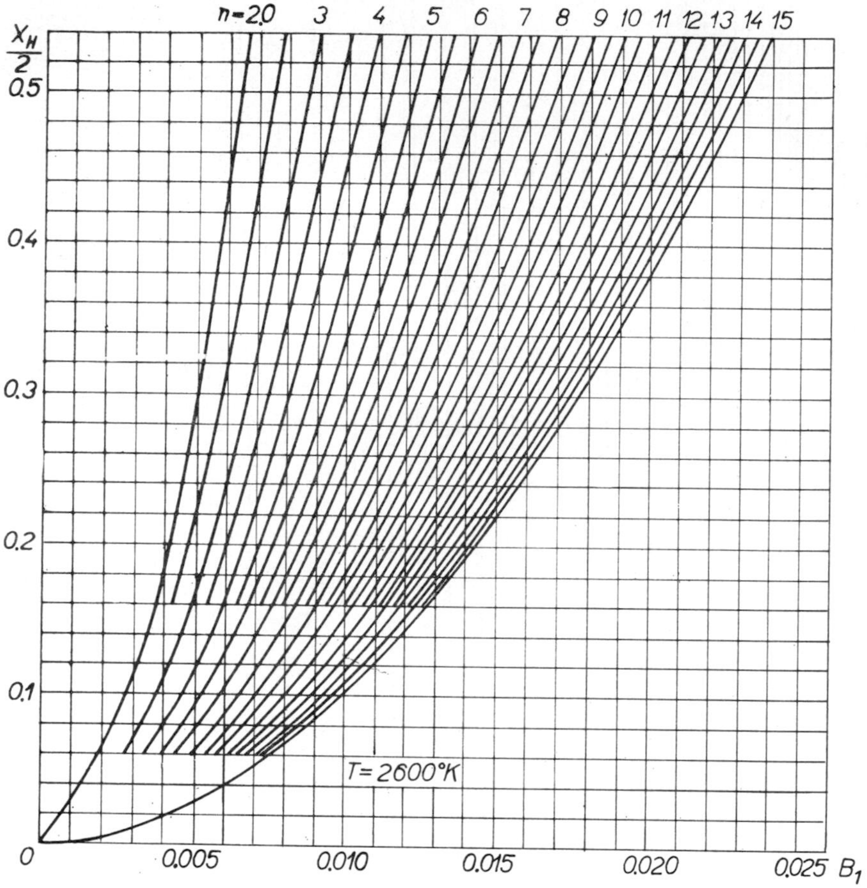
n=2.0
3
4
5
6
7
8
9
10
11
12
13
14
15
$\frac{X_H}{2}$
0.5
0.4
0.3
0.2
0.1
0
0.005
0.010
0.015
0.020
0.025
B_1
T=2600°K

FIG. 35

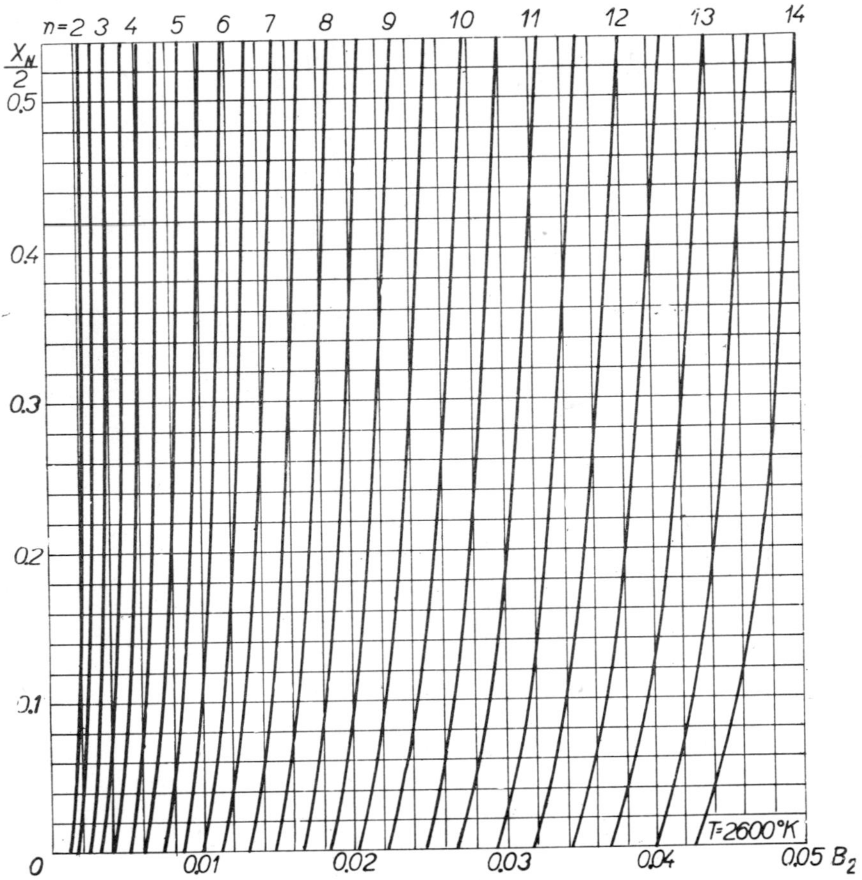

n=2 3 4 5 6 7 8 9 10 11 12 13 14
$\frac{X_N}{2}$
0.5
0.4
0.3
0.2
0.1
0
0.01
0.02
0.03
0.04
0.05 B_2
T=2600°K

FIG. 36

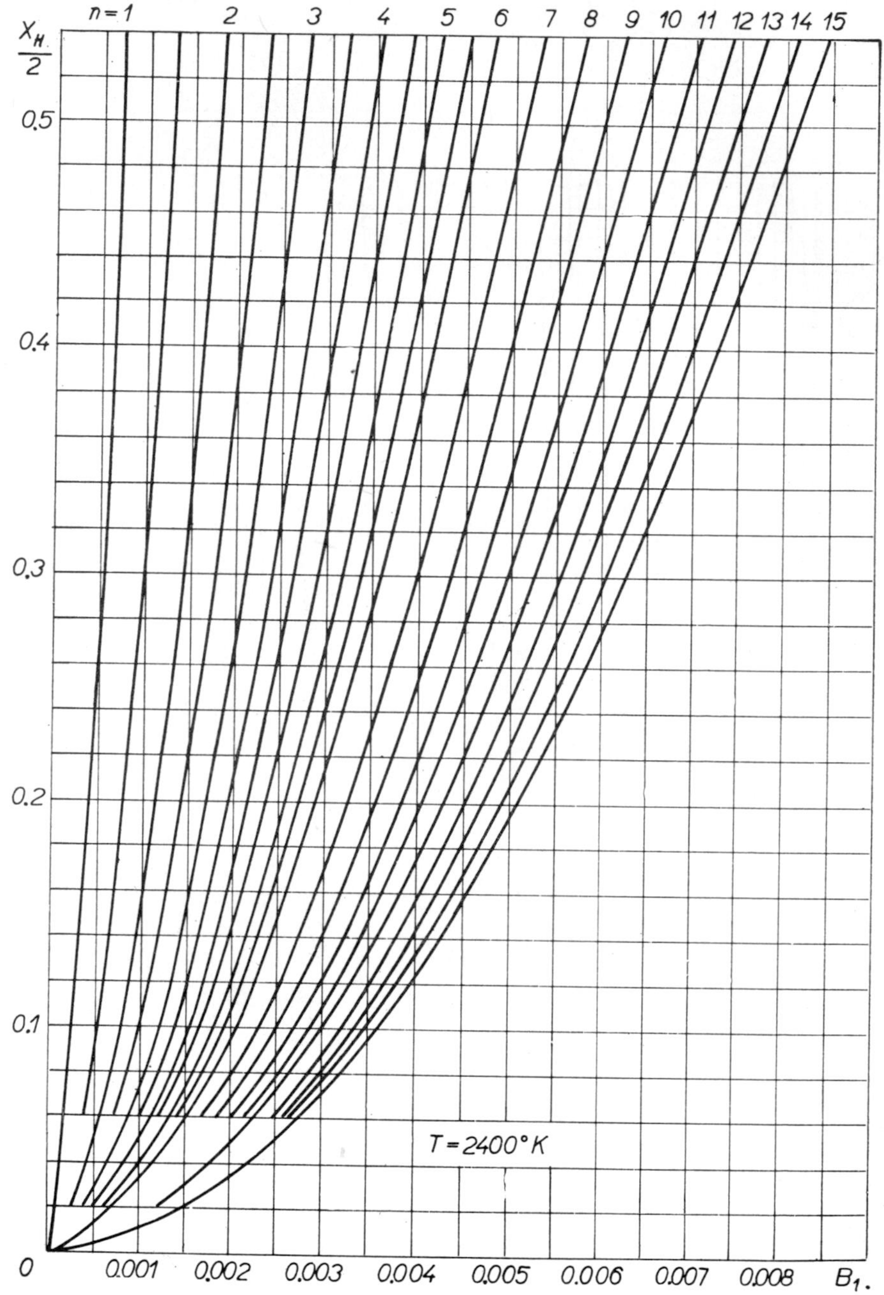
n = 1
2
3
4
5
6
7
8
9
10
11
12
13
14
15
X_H/2
0.5
0.4
0.3
0.2
0.1
0
0.001
0.002
0.003
0.004
0.005
0.006
0.007
0.008
B_1.
T = 2400° K

FIG. 37

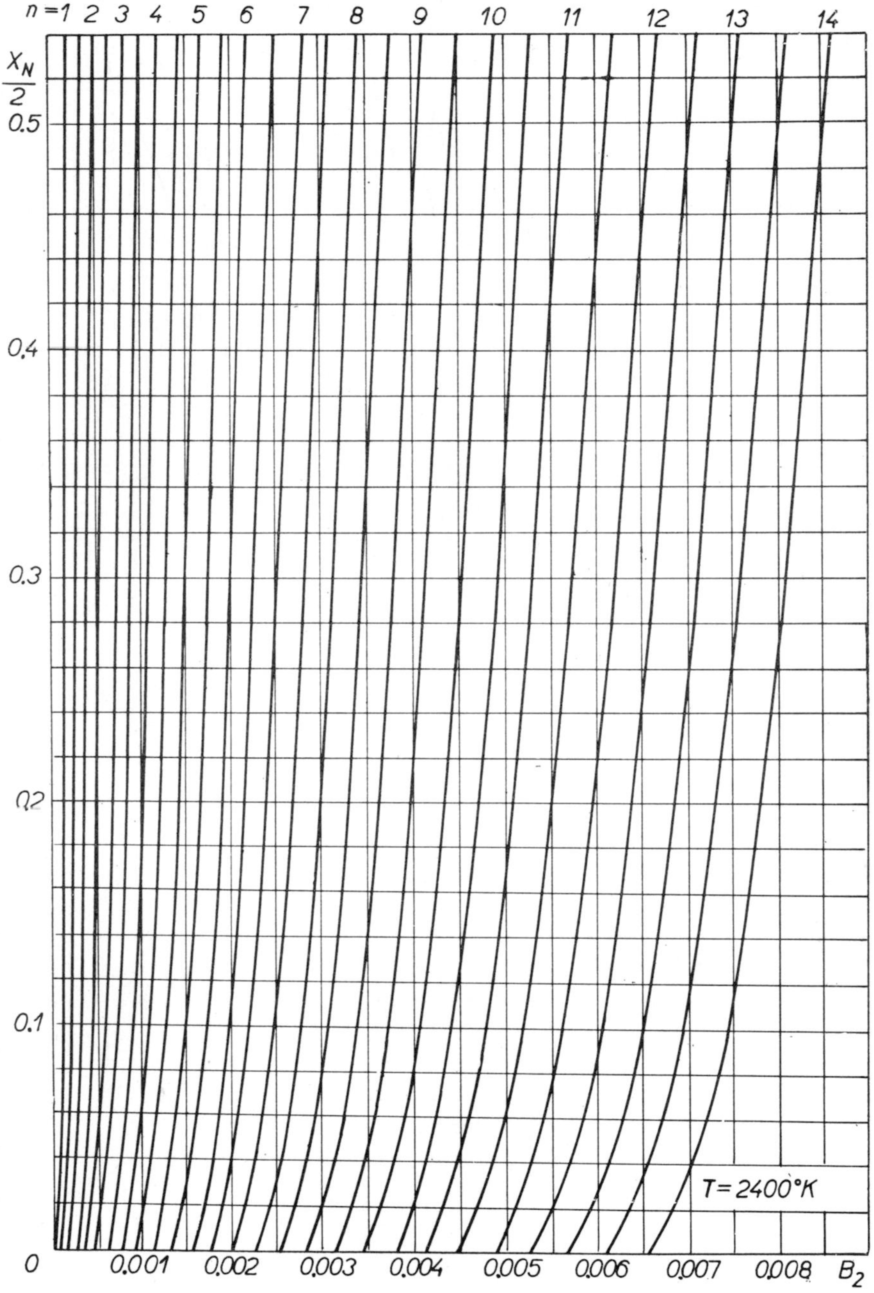
n = 1 2 3 4 5 6 7 8 9 10 11 12 13 14
$\frac{X_N}{2}$
0.5
0.4
0.3
0.2
0.1
0
0.001 0.002 0.003 0.004 0.005 0.006 0.007 0.008 B_2
T = 2400°K

FIG. 38

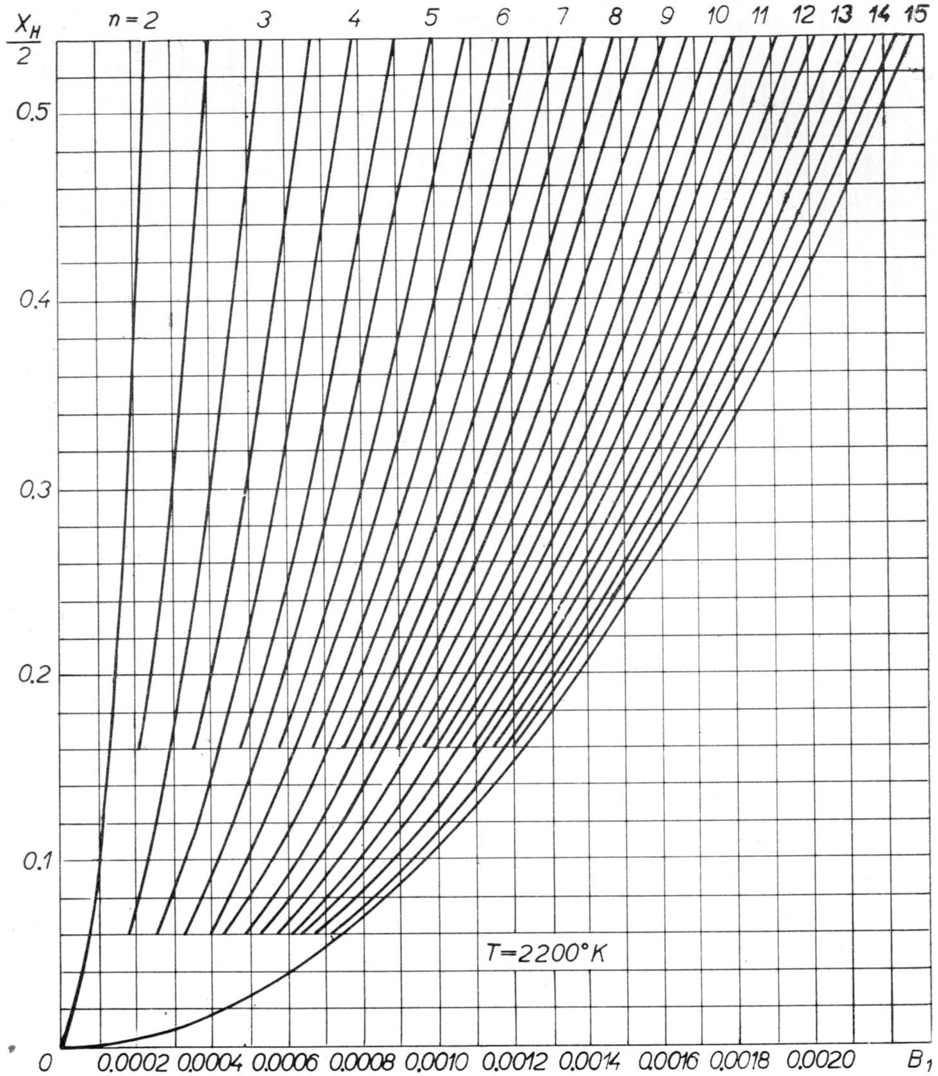
$\frac{X_H}{2}$
n = 2
3
4
5
6
7
8
9
10
11
12
13
14
15
0.5
0.4
0.3
0.2
0.1
0
0.0002
0.0004
0.0006
0.0008
0.0010
0.0012
0.0014
0.0016
0.0018
0.0020
B_1
T=2200°K

FIG. 39

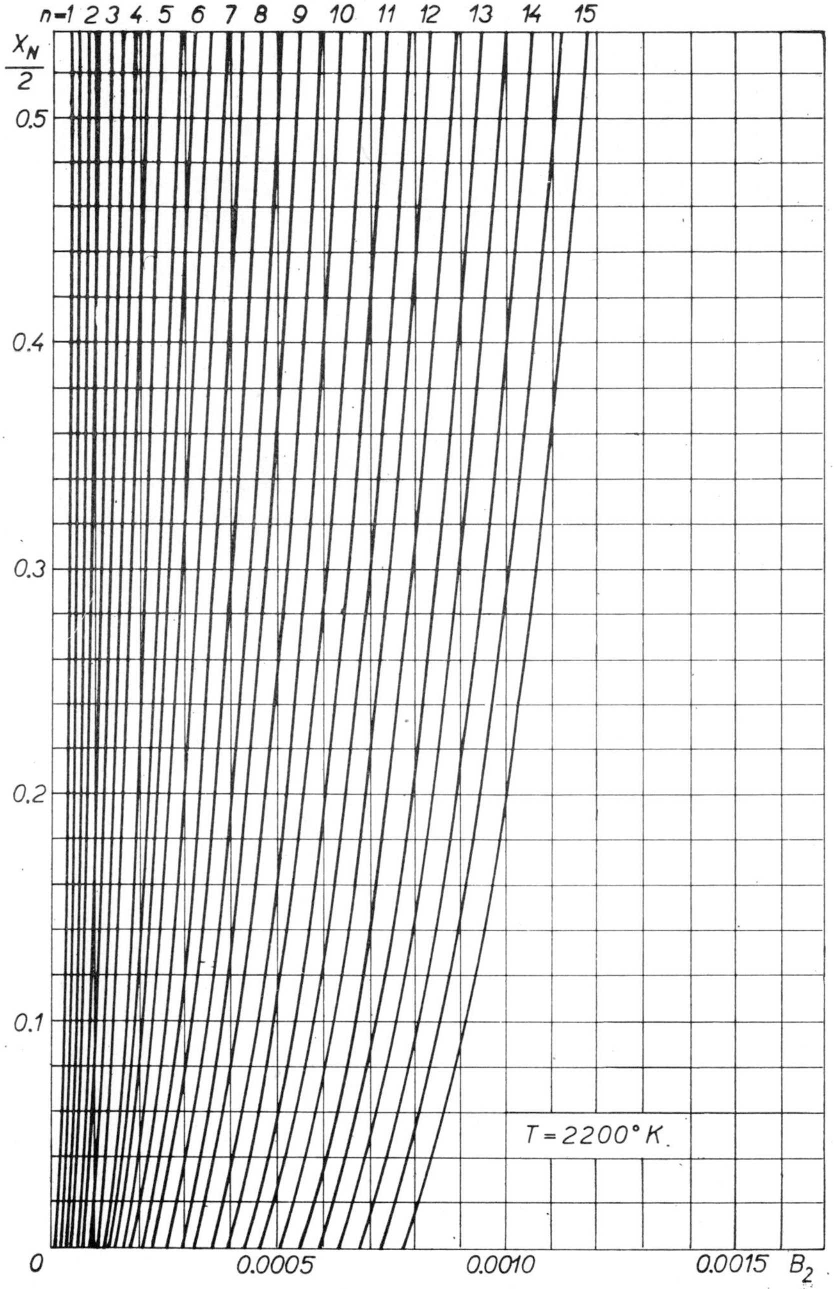
n=1 2 3 4 5 6 7 8 9 10 11 12 13 14 15
$\frac{X_N}{2}$
0.5
0.4
0.3
0.2
0.1
0
0.0005
0.0010
0.0015
B_2
T = 2200° K.

Fig. 40

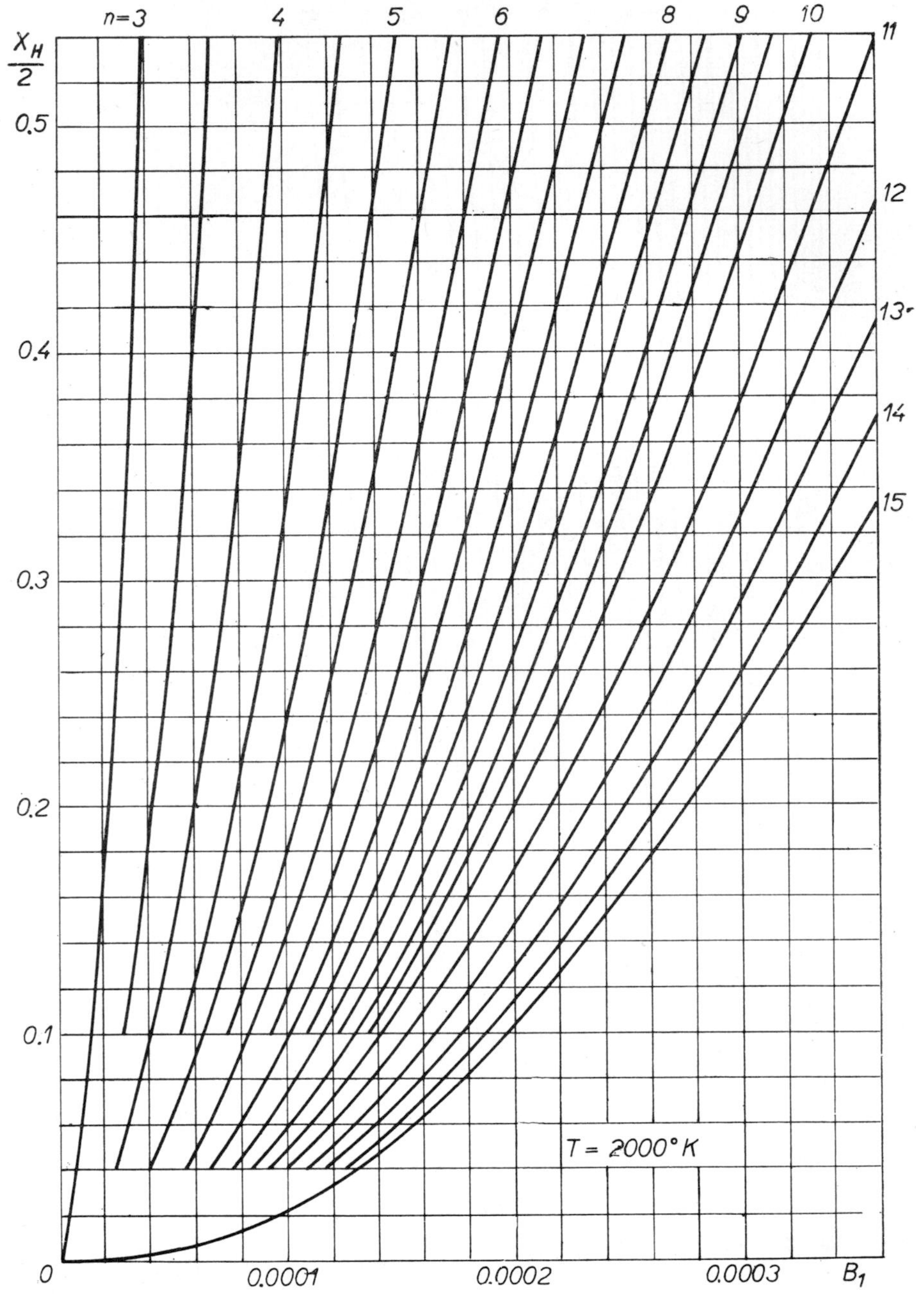
n=3
4
5
6
8
9
10
11
12
13
14
15
$\frac{X_H}{2}$
0.5
0.4
0.3
0.2
0.1
0
0.0001
0.0002
0.0003
B_1
T = 2000° K

FIG. 41

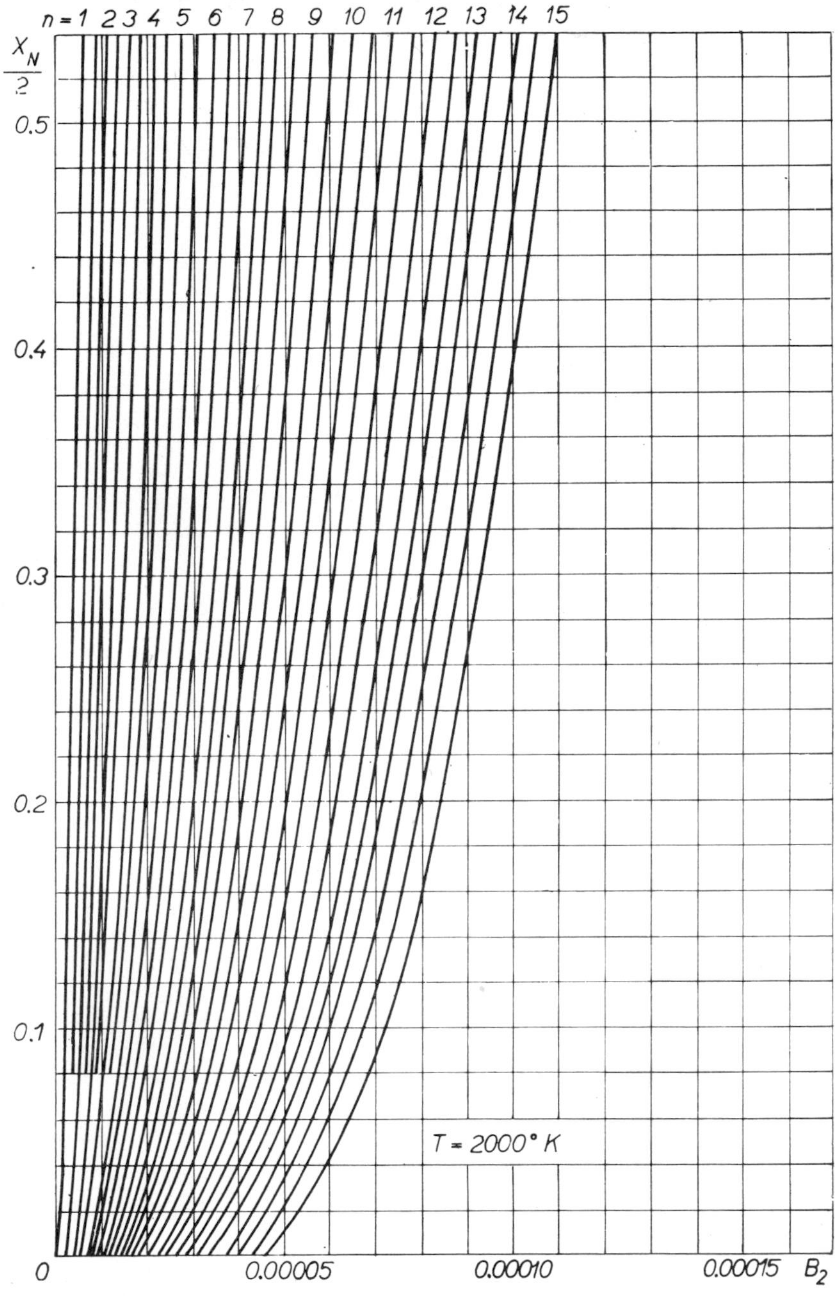
n = 1 2 3 4 5 6 7 8 9 10 11 12 13 14 15
$\frac{X_N}{2}$
0.5
0.4
0.3
0.2
0.1
0
0.00005
0.00010
0.00015
B_2
T = 2000° K

FIG. 42

Index

THE ROYAL COLLEGE OF SCIENCE AND TECHNOLOGY
ANDERSONIAN LIBRARY
GLASGOW

THE ROYAL COLLEGE OF SCIENCE AND TECHNOLOGY
ANDERSONIAN
LIBRARY
GLASGOW